CU00692937

SUPERPOWER
BRITAIN

SUPERPOWER
·B·R·I·T·A·I·N·

Roy Sherwood

Willingham Press

TO DOREEN

First published in Great Britain in 1989 by
Willingham Press
22 Schole Road, Willingham
Cambridge CB4 5JD

Copyright © Roy Sherwood 1989

ISBN 0 9514113 0 6

British Library Cataloguing in Publication Data
Sherwood, Roy
  Superpower Britain.
  1. Great Britain, 1945
  I. Title
  941.085

  ISBN 0-9514113-0-6

Production and design in association with
Book Production Consultants, Cambridge.

Typeset by Cambridge Photosetting Services.
Printed in England by The Burlington Press (Cambridge) Ltd.
Cover picture: Tony Stone Photolibrary, London.

CONTENTS

ILLUSTRATIONS

I would like to thank the following for the trouble they took in supplying me with these illustrations and for giving me permission to reproduce them: British Aerospace (1, 7, 9); Imperial War Museum, London (10); Royal Air Force Museum, Hendon (2, 3, 6); United Kingdom Atomic Energy Authority (11, 12, 13); Westland Aerospace (8); Westland Helicopters Limited (4, 5).

ACKNOWLEDGEMENTS

Although no attempt has been made before to chart the course of Britain's advanced technology since World War II, and certainly not within the context of the country's postwar decline, important works do exist on single aspects of that technology. These have proved invaluable in the writing of this book. I feel, however, that it would be invidious to single out individual titles for special mention here. I trust, therefore, that their inclusion in the bibliography will suffice as a record of my indebtedness.

My thanks are due to the staff of the University Library, Cambridge, where this book was largely written; Mrs Gillian Lee, who in typing the first draft of the manuscript undertook the difficult task of deciphering my handwriting with unfailing patience; Mrs Susan Craft, who typed the succeeding drafts; and my wife, Doreen, for her considerable practical assistance and unerring support. I also wish to thank Debbie Wright and Peter Dolton of Book Production Consultants, Cambridge.

Roy Sherwood

The writing of history must always
take into account lost visions and
lost hopes, the world that might
have been but never was.

Roy Strong,
*Henry, Prince of Wales and
England's Lost Renaissance*

1

INTRODUCTION

Britain as a superpower? The idea seems fantastic, even absurd, in the light of the country's present position as a relatively impoverished minor military and industrial power. And yet only a generation ago, in the nineteen fifties, Britain did indeed stand shoulder to shoulder with the United States and the Soviet Union.

How was this possible? It was possible because whatever else she may have lacked in relation to America and Russia Britain more than made up for in the possession of the one essential ingredient in superpower status, *superpower technology*. Not only that, Britain was actually years ahead of the Americans and Russians in the development and exploitation of certain branches of this technology, much of which was of British invention in the first place.

Britain led the world in aeronautics, both military and civil, and in most of the other applications of the jet engine, whether it was to power cars and ships or to generate electricity. Britain's missile technology was on a par with that of the United States and the Soviet Union and consequently so was her space capability, so much so

1

that Britain could have put an astronaut into space within a very few years of the first American and Russian spacemen. Britain also led the world in the exploitation of atomic power for peaceful purposes and demonstrated her parity with America and Russia in the development of the hydrogen bomb.

Possession of superpower technology had a very special significance for early postwar Britain. It was seen as a replacement for the previous benefits of empire and the Industrial Revolution and the means whereby the nation's military and industrial decline could be checked. The country would enjoy a New Elizabethan Age of greatness and prosperity through the exploitation of the most advanced technology known to man.

Britain was, in fact, widely seen as having no real choice but to grasp the technological opportunities which lay in the palm of her hand. It was the only possible way forward. The alternative was both chilling and uncompromising: the nation's consequent decline would be absolute and irrevocable.

And yet, incredible though it may seem, steps were taken which would effectively check Britain's advance in those vital fields of aerospace and nuclear power, thus earning for Britain the dubious distinction of being perhaps the only country in history purposefully to downgrade its own technology.

This is the story of the rise and fall of British advanced technology since World War II. It is a tale of bright vision and high endeavour eclipsed by incompetence, ignorance and blind stupidity. It is also the story of a crime, a crime perpetrated by Britain's decision makers against the people of Britain.

2

AERONAUTICS

Zenith

The undisputed symbol of Britain's postwar aeronautical supremacy, and of the country's self-image in the New Elizabethan Age, was the Comet airliner. This aircraft, with its outstandingly exquisite aerodynamic form, made history in May 1952 when it became the world's first pure jet airliner to go into regular passenger service, less than two years and ten months after its first flight. A medium-haul airliner, the Comet was capable of travelling at 500 mph at a height of 40,000 feet and so smoothly that a coin could be balanced on edge on a passenger's table. It brought a completely new dimension to civil aviation, which made the shortness of the period between the Comet's first flight and its arrival on the regular passenger scene all the more remarkable. Such speeds at such altitudes had been first achieved less than a decade earlier, and then only by a small group of specially trained men under hazardous circumstances.

Perhaps not surprisingly therefore the Comet was *the* aeronautical sensation of the nineteen fifties. It stirred the public imagination as no aircraft had done since the beginnings of manned flight some fifty years earlier. With flying times cut by over half, international travel, or rather international travel by Comet, would henceforth be measured in hours instead of days. It was a situation which brought in equal measure joy to the British Overseas Airways Corporation, under whose flag the Comet first flew, and consternation to the rest of the world's airline operators whose aircraft were still lumbering, juddering, piston-engined, petrol-driven affairs of the flying machine age.

The Comet also brought consternation to foreign, and specifically American, aircraft manufacturers as airlines like Pan American, Air France, Canadian Pacific and Japan Air Lines jostled one another in the queue to buy this aeronautical phenomenon. In the midst of an epidemic of Comet fever, skilfully orchestrated from Britain, searching enquiries were being made in the United States and questions asked in the American Senate and House of Representatives as to how it was that the British had been allowed to steal such a march on the United States aviation industry, which now found itself standing in the slips while Britain streaked ahead into the aeronautical future.

And what a march it was: it would be another six-and-a-half years before the first American pure jet airliner, the Boeing 707, entered scheduled passenger service and over four years before the world's second pure jet airliner, the Russian Tupolev Tu-104, did the same. What is more, the Americans and Russians would owe much both to the lessons learned by Britain with the Comet and to experience gained from their own jet bombers, experience that was simply not available when the Comet first flew.

But what must have been particularly galling for the Americans was the fact that during the war it was agreed that the United States should concentrate on transport aircraft and Britain on warplanes. In the process, so it has

4

been claimed, while British aeronautical technology and expertise was made freely available to the United States the Americans kept theirs to themselves. And *still* the British were able to steal that incredible six-and-a-half-year postwar lead over the United States in the development of transport aircraft.

This lead was not confined to the Comet either. There was also the short-haul Viscount and the long-haul Britannia. Both of these were turboprop-powered airliners whose gas-turbine engines, unlike those of the pure jet Comet, were used to drive propellers. This resulted in faster, quieter, more vibration-free and more economical flight than was possible in the conventional petrol-driven piston-engined aircraft. The Viscount would subsequently become Britain's most commercially successful civil aircraft and enter the annals of aviation history as one of the truly great aircraft of its time. Its big brother, the Britannia, was the first long-haul turbine-powered transport. It was also the world's largest, most economical and quietest (for which it earned the sobriquet Whispering Giant) airliner and would establish a number of impressive records including a new distance record for a civil aircraft of 6100 miles in 1957.

At the end of 1952 construction work on these three airliners, the pure jet Comet and the turboprop Viscount and Britannia, was given 'super priority'. This was part of an unprecedented production programme designed to ensure that orders could be met on time as Britain was, it seemed, poised to capture a massive slice of the world market for short, medium and long-haul transports. In the case of the Comet, one government minister expressed the belief that the lead in civil jet aviation which this aircraft represented meant that Britain 'will possibly "collar" the market for a generation'.

At the same time, Britain's unrivalled tradition in building bombers and her unequalled penchant for inventiveness combined to produce the spectacular

Valiant, Vulcan and Victor V-bombers. These entered RAF service in the nineteen fifties and represented Britain's heavy jet bomber force with nuclear capability. All three types of V-bomber were sublime studies in symmetry and power and broke entirely new ground in aerodynamics. The Vulcan, for instance, was a huge futuristic-looking flying triangle. It had the distinction of being the world's first, and only wholly successful, large delta-wing aircraft. The Victor, distinguished by its crescent wing shape, was so fast that one accidentally broke the sound barrier in 1957, making it the largest aircraft at that time to fly faster than sound. Without doubt the V-bombers were a striking manifestation of Britain's military aeronautical supremacy in the nineteen fifties. They certainly had no equal in either America or Russia.

The unique four-engined V-bombers were not for sale to overseas buyers. Other British warplanes, however, most certainly were. These included two of the most successful aircraft of the fifties decade, and indeed of the postwar era, the Canberra bomber and the Hunter fighter. The twin-engined Canberra was the world's first medium jet bomber and was responsible for keeping the world altitude record for a manned aircraft continuously in British hands from 1953 until 1958. More than a dozen foreign governments would buy the Canberra. It was also built under licence in America as the B-57 for the US Air Force (there being no suitable American alternative) and was still being used operationally in Vietnam some twenty years later. As for the Hunter fighter, which broke the world air speed record in Coronation year, 1953, this was said to be 'as graceful as it was deadly', as well as being acclaimed 'the world's finest aircraft' and 'the first choice of the RAF and NATO'. Like the Canberra bomber, the number of Hunter fighters produced ran into four figures and it would see service with over twenty of the world's air forces.

Many more warplanes than these were produced by

British aircraft manufacturers in the nineteen fifties and they got better and better as the decade progressed. There was, for instance, the Javelin day and night fighter. This, 'the most formidable aircraft of its type in the world', entered service with the RAF in 1956 as the first ever operational delta-wing aircraft. Following the Javelin into RAF service was 'one of the best aircraft in the world', the Lightning fighter, capable of flying at twice the speed of sound.

There were also naval warplanes for Britain's almost twenty-strong fleet of aircraft carriers, which included two fifty-thousand tonners carrying a hundred planes apiece. The Scimitar was said to be the fastest and most powerful naval fighter in the world when it made its first flight in 1951. The Sea Hawk was regarded as one of the most graceful naval fighters ever built and the most modern when it entered service with the Royal Navy in 1953. The Sea Vixen was the first two-seater aircraft to fly faster than sound, while the Buccaneer naval bomber was estimated to have put Britain three years ahead of the rest of the world in the field of high-speed, low-level strike aircraft at the time of its maiden flight in 1958.

The engines which propelled these British fighters, bombers and airliners, as well as ancillary equipment, were to be bought, or built under licence, by a number of other countries for their own aircraft. The biggest overseas customer was the United States. Among the engines taken up with alacrity by the Americans was the Bristol Olympus. This was the most powerful jet engine in the world at the time of its unveiling in 1952. Twenty years later the Olympus would be used in Concorde, its power in the intervening years having been increased almost eight-fold, the largest growth in power of an aero-engine ever achieved.

But then the world's first practical jet engine, patented in 1930 by its ex-RAF apprentice inventor Sir Frank Whittle, had been British, as was the only Allied jet aircraft to see service in World War II. And it was with British jet fighters that most of the world's air forces were re-equipped in the immediate postwar years. Neither the United States nor the Soviet Union had developed jet engines of their own. Instead they relied initially on the procurement of British engines and these would provide the basis for future American and Russian gas-turbine technology.

In helicopters too Britain was poised to grab a major portion of the world market. She also assumed a pioneering role in the use of the helicopter. In the early fifties there were experimental projects such as inter-city passenger flights and overnight mail delivery, while during the Suez campaign of 1956, in a singular example of derring-do, Royal Marine commandos carried out what has been described as history's first helicopter-borne assault.

It seemed in the nineteen fifties that there was nothing in the field of aeronautics that the country could not accomplish. Aircraft manufacture was seen as one of the ways forward for Britain, especially as the nation's more traditional industries were already under threat from rising foreign competitors who had nothing in the way of advanced aeronautical technology with which to compete with the British.

Britain's aeronautical feast was, however, not without its skeleton. On Saturday 6 September 1952 disaster struck. It struck on a day of record crowds at the then all-British annual Farnborough air display. A de Havilland DH110 (later to enter Royal Navy service as the Sea Vixen) being put through its paces by the celebrated test pilot John Derry suddenly disintegrated in mid-air. One of its spiralling white-hot engines plunged into the densest section of the crowd, killing thirty people and injuring another sixty. After a short break the display continued and the number of spectators attending the following and last day was to be the highest in the history of the show. Nothing, but nothing, it would seem, could overshadow the achievement of the nation's breathtaking technological advance and the reflected glory that Britons gained from it.

In hindsight it is as if the Farnborough air disaster, the first major accident ever to happen at a public air display, was an omen both for the nation and for Britain's aeronautical supremacy. Within a matter of months calamity struck again, this time at the very heart of the British aircraft industry. Three Comet airliners literally fell, one by one, out of the sky, killing everyone on board. All three accidents were not only identical in almost every detail but they were also totally inexplicable.

After the third disaster all Comets were grounded. Between them they had travelled no less than eight million miles in just under two years. The effect of the Comet calamity on Britain's pride was catastrophic and it took more than a little steam out of the ebullience that characterized the first few years of the New Elizabethan Age, of which this particular aeronautical triumph had been seen as so much a part.

Speculation as to the cause of the accidents became rife and it was not long before the word sabotage entered the vocabulary of speculation. Next came the finger of suspicion, pointed unhesitatingly and publicly by some at the Americans who, it was suggested, might very well have been driven to this desperate deed out of blind jealousy. But after the most exhaustive tests ever known the real cause of the disasters was found. Structural failure of the pressure cabin had occurred at one corner of a window causing explosive decompression. This was a design problem which the test and certification procedures of the time were unable to anticipate. In technology there is sometimes a price to be paid for being first and Britain had paid it in full, as had those pioneer jetliner passengers who died. Nevertheless it is generally recognized that every jet airliner flying today owes its existence to the lessons learned from this ill-fated aeronautical phenomenon from the days of Britain's supremacy in the air.

Blunder and Confusion

There was, however, another blow to come, one that would ultimately prove far more devastating than the Comet disasters. Incredible though it may seem the buoyant and successful ship that was the British aircraft industry in the early fifties began, by the second half of the decade, to spring a leak as Blunder assumed command and Confusion took the helm.

To begin with there was the monumental blunder which irrevocably affected Britain's jet airliner programme. Late in 1952 work had begun on the construction of what would have been the world's first long-haul big jet transport capable of carrying up to 150 passengers the 3000 miles across the Atlantic. (The Comet could carry only 44 passengers over a maximum distance of 1750 miles.) Developed from the Valiant V-bomber, the military version, to be used by the RAF as a troop and freight carrier, was given the designation V1000 and the civil version VC7. With this second generation pure jet transport, aimed at the lucrative North Atlantic traffic, Britain looked set to maintain her already considerable world lead in civil aviation. But three years later, in November 1955, within months of the V1000/VC7's first flight, governmental policy miscalculations, based on muddled thinking and short-term financial considerations, intervened. The project was cancelled.

Meanwhile painstaking research into the ill-fated Comet project had been continuing, resulting in a substantially rebuilt aircraft, the larger, long-range Comet 4. In October 1958 this aeronautical phoenix inaugurated the long-awaited first North Atlantic pure jet service.

Even so, the Comet 4 could still only accommodate 76 passengers and was therefore not a 'big' jet.

The 180-seat Boeing 707, with which the Americans inaugurated *their* transatlantic pure jet service just three weeks after the Comet 4, and its later compatriot the DC8 were, however, most certainly big jet airliners. Naturally the advent of these large American jets in the late nineteen fifties totally eclipsed the Comet 4, of which only 74 were to be built. They also eclipsed the turboprop Britannia. The irony was that the cancelled British VC7 big jet airliner would not only have entered service before the American Boeing 707 and the DC8 but it was also a superior aircraft.

In an attempt to rectify matters design work was begun all over again on a British long-haul big jet transport sixteen months after the cancellation of the VC7. The result was the VC10. This incorporated many of the features of the VC7, although unlike the VC7 it had tail-mounted engines, the first long-range airliner in the world to be so designed. Universally admired, the VC10 consistently carried higher percentage loads than its competitors but only 54 were to be built and in consequence the plane did not even recover its development costs. In contrast the numbers produced of its American rivals ran into four figures. But then the transatlantic version of the VC10 did not enter service until 1965, by which time the commercial initiative had long since passed to the United States. There plans were already about to be put in hand for the development of double capacity jumbo jets in response to the spectacular growth in air travel that was a feature of the nineteen sixties. It was a situation American manufacturers were able to take full advantage of while the late-in-the-day British merely picked up the crumbs from off the table.

That fateful decision of November 1955 to cancel the V1000/VC7 long-range big jet project when Britain was literally years ahead in airline development, thus leaving the field wide open to the Americans, is now universally recognized as a major turning point for British aeronautics. It was indeed the greatest of blunders and, as one cabinet minister admitted, 'a terrible tragedy'. And it was a blunder and a tragedy from which Britain's aircraft industry was destined never to recover.

The abandonment of the V1000/VC7 airliner had, however, much wider implications than the cancellation of just another aeronautical project. It has been suggested that it represented a loss of nerve on the part of Britain's decision makers who had been so traumatized by the Comet disasters that they saw jets as dangerous things whose development ought not to be pursued.

The V1000/VC7 though was not to be the only victim of gross miscalculation. Another area where Britain had seemed poised to capture a massive slice of the world's markets early in the fifties decade was that of the short to medium-haul airliner. Success here had been assured by the Viscount, which entered regular passenger service in 1953. Although the Viscount was not a pure jet but a turboprop (the world's first) the time gap that it filled prior to the arrival on the scene of the pure jet equivalent was considerable, unlike its long-haul big brother the Britannia, and resulted in an impressive world-wide sales record. Its successor was to be another turboprop, the Vanguard. But someone had blundered because by the time the Vanguard entered service in the early nineteen sixties pure jets were very much the vogue. Consequently the plane enjoyed little commercial success.

Once again an attempt was made to rectify matters with what was to become the pure jet Trident. Massive worldwide sales were predicted by the manufacturers for this short to medium-haul airliner. On the strength of what proved to be a miscalculation in future passenger growth, however, the Trident specification was altered, reducing its size and in the process its appeal to world markets. It first flew early in 1962, becoming the world's first triple-jet airliner to fly. Even so, its much larger, and therefore more acceptable, American rival, the Boeing 727, beat the Trident into regular passenger service. Only about 120 Tridents were to be sold; a pathetic result when compared with Boeing 727 sales of over 2000. Ironically it has been claimed that the Americans feared the original Trident concept and that a proper handling of the plane's development at its inception might have persuaded them to abandon what was to become the all-time best-selling Boeing 727. It has also been claimed that the Americans were naively given access to British Trident research which they incorporated into the 727.

Although many civil aircraft projects were mooted throughout the nineteen sixties Britain was destined to build only one more airliner of any size. This was the 100-seat short to medium-haul BAC One-Eleven. The first foreign aircraft to be ordered 'off the drawing board' by a US airline, the One-Eleven entered regular passenger service in 1965. Yet sales, although excellent by previous British standards, could not match those of the One-Eleven's two American rivals, the Boeing 737 and the DC9, both of which entered service later than the British plane, one of them almost three years later. A couple of initial set-backs were blamed for blighting the One-Eleven's chances. Perhaps equally as important though was the fact that since the late nineteen fifties the United States had become popularly identified with advanced civil aeronautics just as Britain had been earlier in the decade.

The decisions that effectively sounded the death-knell of Britain as a manufacturer of civil aircraft were certainly bizarre. But by comparison the decision that effectively sounded the knell of Britain as a manufacturer of military aircraft was nothing short of grotesque. One of the precepts of the post-Suez Defence White Paper of April 1957 was that future wars would be nuclear wars. Manned military aircraft were therefore obsolete. This assumption had originated in the United States but unlike their American counterparts British policy makers swallowed the theory hook, line and sinker and implemented it almost to the full. Consequently a veritable galaxy of bright stars in the form of British military aircraft of revolutionary design were in one way or another extinguished. They represented years of painstaking research and a massive financial investment.

Among the cancelled projects was the P177, a high-performance jet fighter equipped with rocket motors for climb boost and assisted take off. The Japanese had shown particular interest in this rocket-plus-jet plane. So too had the West Germans who hoped to build it under licence in order to re-equip their nascent air force with a truly advanced fighter and at the same time create an advanced technology base on which to build up their embryo aircraft industry. With the abandonment of the P177 by the British the Japanese and West Germans were forced to procure in considerable quantity a much inferior American plane.

Extinguished too was one of the most remarkable aeronautical projects of its time, the Fairey Delta 2, also known as the Flying Dart. In March 1956 this plane increased the world air speed record from 822 mph to 1132 mph at a stroke. Never before had the record been raised by such a margin. The shock waves were felt throughout the entire aeronautical world and especially in the United States where the initial response was one of near incredulity. It had been envisaged that a whole 'family' of aircraft would be developed from the Flying Dart, each 'member' being adapted to a different role, but the cancellation of the project put an end to all that. The French, however, utilized data from the Flying Dart by incorporating it into their Mirage project, one of the most successful 'family' of military aircraft (ranging from fighter to scaled-up nuclear bomber) ever to be built.

Perhaps predictably the fate that befell Britain's

advance in the fields of military and civil aircraft was to be shared by the country's ambitious helicopter programme. Of the very many truly advanced British helicopter projects of the nineteen fifties none showed greater promise than the revolutionary Rotodyne. This was a hybrid airliner/helicopter, or compound helicopter, being in effect a twin-engined aeroplane topped by a rotor blade. Numerous military and civil applications were mooted for the graceful Rotodyne, which was in fact the world's first vertical take-off and landing transport. Among them were its use as a car ferry and as an ideal machine for a London to Paris, centre-to-centre, passenger service. As a flying crane it was able to lift 1000 feet-long girder bridges. In addition to all these attributes the Rotodyne, which first flew in 1957, established a new world speed record for helicopters in 1959. But in spite of the keen interest this unique British project generated on both sides of the Atlantic, the Rotodyne fell victim to the now all too familiar policy miscalculations and was abandoned in 1962. A few years later the minister responsible for the Rotodyne's cancellation would admit the folly of his action by stating that if the project had not been killed inter-city helicopter services would have become a regular and popular feature of British life.

There were other British helicopter projects but the main trend was towards British-built machines developed from American designs, supplemented later by French, Anglo-French and even Anglo-Italian developments. This was in spite of the excellence of some of the British products and Britain's pioneering role, expansively and expensively pursued in this particular field.

Nadir

No sooner had the drastic conclusion been reached that manned military aircraft were obsolete than its essential flaws became apparent. It was now foreseen that future wars would not necessarily be all-nuclear or nothing and that military activity of various sorts, including small-scale wars, would probably continue within the conventional sphere. Also, it was well recognized that the military branch of aeronautics had provided much of the impetus for truly spectacular advances in aircraft development, and these in turn had fed civil aeronautical projects.

But like the cancellation of the V1000/VC7 big jet airliner in 1955, when Britain was ahead in the field, the post-Suez pause in the nation's military aircraft programme meant that the Americans were able to catch up with, and subsequently overtake, Britain in warplane development. It was yet another governmental blunder from which the British aircraft industry would never totally recover.

Three projects to emerge after the 1957 Defence White Paper were a supersonic bomber, the TSR2 (Tactical Strike and Reconnaissance Aircraft), a supersonic VTOL (vertical take-off and landing) jet fighter, and a short take-off and landing troop and cargo jet transport. Between them these three aircraft would, it was said, provide the RAF with 'the finest integrated all-round equipment in the world'.

The TSR2, work on which began in 1959, was, however, the only one of the three actually to fly. It was considered miles in advance of anything the Americans had even dreamed of. Indeed, it was reputedly the most sophisticated aircraft ever built. And at a time when Britain was considering American-supplied delivery systems for her principal deterrent to replace the V-bombers (*see* Chapter 4) the TSR2 would ensure some degree of continuing independent nuclear capability. Also, the plane could, it was felt, have considerable overseas sales potential. The same was said of its two 'sister' projects.

Nevertheless, after an expenditure of hundreds of millions of pounds and electoral promises to the contrary, all three projects were cancelled within six months of the coming to power of Harold Wilson's Labour government in October 1964. This 1965 decision, which resulted in a furore of unprecedented proportions, has been described as a massive blow struck at the British aircraft industry. But it was really a *coup de grâce* because the main damage had already been done in the nineteen fifties.

Paradoxically in that same year of 1965 a government inspired inquiry into the British aircraft industry, the Plowden Committee on Aviation, estimated that military projects (like the ones cancelled) would represent 80 per cent of the total aircraft market for at least the next twenty-five years. There was also, of course, the importance of the military sector to the civil aircraft industry in terms of technical stimulus. Nevertheless the Plowden Committee saw little potential for increased sales of large, wholly British, advanced military aircraft, although it was felt that there might still be scope for a few smaller all-British types. The committee thus recommended that Britain should meet any future requirements for large advanced military planes from American sources. And this is precisely what happened. Instead of the TSR2 bomber, the supersonic VTOL fighter and the short take-off and landing jet transport the RAF was told that it would have to make do with infinitely less sophisticated off-the-shelf equivalents from the United States, one of which never actually materialized.

Between them those three abandoned British projects would come to represent the apogee of those skills and expertise of the British aircraft industry that had burgeoned in the fifties decade. Their cancellation signalled the end of Britain as an independent manufacturer of truly advanced military aircraft. The irony is that such was the advanced nature of the TSR2 and its 'sister' projects that nothing approaching them had entered service anywhere in the world twenty years after their cancellation.

Another irony is that before becoming prime minister in 1964 Harold Wilson had spoken of 'the new technological revolution' which was bringing about technical change, particularly in industrial methods, greater than the whole industrial revolution of the previous 250 years. He had also spoken of 'the Britain that is going to be forged in the white heat of this revolution' in which scientific research would be applied to industrial processes under the aegis of a minister of science, thus providing the answer to the problem of Britain's declining industries. At the same time it was hoped that this would bring about a slowing down, a reversal even, of the 'brain drain' from Britain to the United States.

The aircraft industry itself, however, was very much a part of the 'new technological revolution' whose technology-elevating spin-off benefits affected the widest possible range of other industries. The areas in which the industry pioneered significant developments included computer and electronics engineering, engineering technology, precision plastics and other structural materials. Even the Plowden Committee on Aviation conceded that 'it seems probable that no other single industry would have such a pervasive effect on the technological progress of the nation'. Little wonder therefore that the now shattered British aircraft industry had once been seen as an instrument of Britain's industrial and economic salvation.

Perhaps predictably the Wilson government's 'white hot technological revolution', as it came to be known, fizzled out. The brain drain, which took about one third of the younger engineers leaving the British aircraft industry in the mid-sixties, continued, while other workers were forced into lower technology industries where their talents were under-exploited.

After 1965 the only new front-line military project that

remained to the British aircraft industry was a sub-sonic vertical take-off and landing jet fighter, the Harrier jump jet, work on which had begun in 1959. Throughout the nineteen fifties every apparently feasible VTOL system had received government sponsorship in the United States. And France and West Germany were to build prototypes using British engines. But only Britain's project actually came to anything, although Russia was later to develop a similar, but less successful, VTOL aircraft. Described as 'the most effective all round fighter in existence', the Harrier, with its unique ability to operate without traditional runways or airfields, brought a totally fresh aspect to aviation. For that reason the plane was snapped up by the United States where it would ultimately be built under licence. Without doubt this, in many respects, essentially fifties development was one of the most outstanding examples of Britain's pioneering role in revolutionary aeronautical technique. It was also to be the last.

'America's Tin-bashers'

All too soon the radiant promise with which the British aircraft industry had helped to illuminate the nineteen fifties had dimmed. The sonorous power of the high-performance record-breaking aircraft of that decade was destined to be the swan-song of Britain as a major independent aircraft producer.

Having been forced to desert important areas on the frontiers of knowledge on its own account the British aircraft industry was to become increasingly reliant for its continued existence on collaborative ventures with other countries or subcontract work from foreign, mainly American, manufacturers. Thus, by the nineteen seventies, news of an order for a few hundred inner wing flaps for a new US airliner and a contract to carry out modification work on the ejector seat systems of American military aircraft was being received with almost the same jubilation as had been the announcement of the opening of a production line for an actual aircraft in the past.

Ironically the position of collaborator and subcontractor to which Britain had largely, but not entirely, declined was to be the chosen starting point for Japan's late entry into aeronautics. From these modest beginnings the Japanese are determined to progress to producing large-scale products of their own, including a supersonic airliner capable of flying at twice the speed of sound, a project with which Rolls-Royce would very much like to be associated. Little wonder that this has in turn provoked fears in Britain that Japan will ultimately dominate aircraft manufacture just as she has shipping, cars and motorcycles.

By the early nineteen eighties the principal new civil project of British Aerospace (the consortium in which the bulk of British aeronautical activity is now concentrated) was the 100-seat BAe 146. Much vaunted as the first *British* airliner (of any size) for twenty years when it first appeared in 1981, the BAe 146 was in reality a collaborative venture. Although of British design, it was created in true Frankenstein fashion with two non-British 'risk sharing partners', the four engines, both wings and most of the avionics (40 per cent of the aircraft) coming from America and the tailplane and moving surfaces of the wings from Sweden. This left British Aerospace to assemble the aircraft and produce the fuselage components.

All-British civil aircraft projects are now confined solely to small capacity commuter and executive jets, a field in which Britain has managed to carve out quite a niche for herself. Such activity is, however, indulged in by countries without a large aircraft industry, such as the odd Third World state. It is also the point from which hitherto technologically backward China has begun the process of building up a large-scale, multi-faceted, national aeronautical industry. So it is small beer indeed when compared to the big jet business in which Britain effectively abandoned her stake in the mid-nineteen fifties when she led the world in jet airliner development.

In the fifties BOAC and BEA took out a press advertisement to proclaim to the world that 'British civil aviation is at the top. That is not a pious hope. That is a fact. And, considering the strength of the competition, it is an enormous achievement.' It was a fact exemplified by illustrations of the latest British airliners in BOAC and BEA livery. Today British Airways, the successor to BOAC and BEA (for whom a generation ago only British aircraft had been good enough), has virtually no genuinely all-British aircraft in its fleet. Now it is the turn of an American aircraft manufacturer to extol in the British press the virtue of British Airways in deciding to purchase yet another of *their* aircraft.

True, American aircraft flown by British Airways are powered by Rolls-Royce engines. Rolls-Royce engines also power many American aircraft flown by US airlines. In fact 60 per cent of Rolls-Royce jet engine business emanates from the United States. But the really plum contracts almost invariably go to American aero-engine manufacturers who had, of course, originally set up business with imported British technology. Not only are such firms better able to compete commercially in what is after all their own home market but they also benefit from a very natural tendency among American airline operators to prefer an all-American product. In any event it could most certainly be argued that a future based to such a degree on a reliance on others to provide the means by which aeronautical developments can be exploited – to build aero-engines but not the aircraft to put them in – does not bode well for the British aircraft industry. It could also be argued that this same condition might ultimately distance the industry from the immediate frontiers of advanced technology.

As with large-scale civil projects collaboration is now very much the order of the day for the British aircraft industry in the field of military aviation. The only new advanced military aircraft on which the industry is engaged is the multi-role Tornado, the product of a European consortium comprising Britain, Italy and West Germany. British Aerospace builds the fin, tail and bits of the fuselage and assembles those Tornados destined to be flown by the RAF. Unless one includes the Hawk trainer, which can be adapted for ground attack and has an Anglo-French engine anyhow, the only front line military aircraft under construction in Britain that is wholly and entirely British is that now aging and essentially fifties development, the sub-sonic Harrier jump jet.

Here again the trend has proved inexorable. In 1981 the government announced that Britain would purchase an *American* improved version of the British Harrier, built under licence in the United States as the McDonnell Douglas AV-8B. Britain's own even more advanced version of this unique aircraft would be abandoned in the interests of economy, dictated by the fact that world demand for the Harrier had proved disappointing. Production of the AV-8B was scheduled to be shared between Britain and America with Britain as the inevitable junior partner. Thus Britain was in effect buying back her own invention subject, of course, to the vagaries of a foreign government. At the same time she was totally surrendering to the United States her current lead in this last outstanding example of the country's pioneering role in aeronautics which had resulted in the world's first, and the West's only, operational VTOL aircraft.

Naturally this led to the now customary furore with one prominent aerospace trade union leader, Ken Gill, levelling accusations of hypocrisy at a government which professed a commitment to the country's technological advance. The issue was, in Gill's view, far wider than a choice of aircraft for the RAF. It was about 'whether British Aerospace should even attempt to survive independently of the Americans'. At this rate the British were, he feared, in grave danger of being reduced to the role of 'America's tin-bashers'.

Meanwhile the RAF flies on towards the nineteen nineties with the thirty-year-old obsolete American Phantom fighter; the British Harrier jump jet, soon to be replaced by an American version of the same plane; the multinational multi-role Tornado; and the Anglo-French Jaguar tactical fighter. The main transport/freighter of the RAF is now the medium-range American Hercules dating from the nineteen fifties. This is considered adequate for Britain's go nowhere air force of the last quarter of the twentieth century, which is why the last of the British-made freighters, the much bigger and more modern long-range Belfast, was phased out in the mid-seventies.

This is indeed in stark contrast to the second half of the fifties decade when all the aircraft, bombers, fighters and transports, flown by the RAF were, with only the odd exception, wholly British. As with the aircraft of the Royal Navy (with its then score of aircraft carriers) they represented the most advanced types available and were a manifestation of Britain's technological expertise and, in particular, of the country's then undoubted aeronautical pre-eminence.

The RAF has in any case become positively Ruritanian by nineteen fifties standards. In those fast receding days only the air forces of America and Russia were larger than that of Britain. Then the RAF was spread over all five continents of a world in which power is measured by what is seen. Now the RAF is little more than a contingent of NATO with about the average number of combat aircraft for a European power the size of Britain. (The same diminution has affected the Royal Navy, now reduced to a couple or so mini-aircraft carriers equipped with just a handful of jump jets and helicopters.) Such has been the extent of Britain's breathtaking decline.

There is, however, something highly significant which distinguishes the RAF from some of those continental counterparts with which it must now be compared, and that is the source of most of its aircraft. The Swedish air force, for instance, is equipped with truly advanced front-line aircraft designed and built exclusively in Sweden (albeit powered by British and American engines made under licence). The government of that neutral nation of only eight million souls has consistently set its face against 'buying off the shelf internationally'.

The same philosophy obtains in France where, unlike in Britain, the question of whether the nation's aircraft industry should even attempt to survive independently of the United States is not one which has needed to be asked. Nor have the French needed to consider the danger of becoming nothing more than a nation of tin-bashers for the Americans. In direct contrast to Britain France has, since the nineteen fifties, managed to develop (beginning with British jet engine technology like America and Russia before her) and maintain a highly technological and highly successful aircraft industry based on a positive preference for wholly national products. Thus France has been the chief alternative source to America and Russia of advanced military aircraft for Commonwealth and foreign governments when re-equipping their originally British-furnished air forces. In this role France sees herself as a powerful magnet attracting other countries away from dependence on the US and the USSR, which by extension enhances considerably the international political influence of the French nation.

Naturally the need to promote collaborative projects so that costly development programmes can be shared is well recognized by the French. But unlike Britain, which has become almost totally reliant on such ventures, France, like America, collaborates from a position of strength based on the solid foundations provided by the existence of exclusively national developments. It was the French, for instance, who inspired and led the consortium to build the European Airbus. This project, for which Britain, a somewhat reluctant participant, makes the wings and holds a 20 per cent stake, comprises a whole 'family' of passenger planes, small, wide-bodied and long-haul. It is set to grab a substantial share of the market, including that in the United States, for the thousands of new airliners that will be needed worldwide in the nineteen eighties and nineteen nineties. The European Airbus therefore represents the first serious threat to American domination of the commercial airlines business since Britain's breathtaking, but aborted, aeronautical advance of the early fifties. Perhaps predictably this has provoked cries of 'unfair competition' from the Americans, unused as they are to having their near monopoly challenged. All of which would seem to prove two things, that it is indeed possible to challenge the Americans and win and that success is not necessarily dependent on collaborative ventures as a junior partner with the United States.

Today Farnborough displays are of necessity international affairs. At these biennial shows British aviation products now vie with those of foreign firms for the attention of potential buyers. A far cry indeed from the annual and wholly British displays of the nineteen fifties which, despite the exclusion of the international element, enjoyed a reputation on both sides of the Atlantic as the 'greatest air shows on Earth'.

A legacy of those days is that Britain still possesses the West's second largest aircraft industry (after that of the United States). And yet, ironically, potential buyers at the Farnborough air displays of the nineteen eighties would be hard pressed to find an all-British production bomber, high-performance fighter or decent sized airliner. But the supreme irony lies in the fact that the, by nineteen fifties standards, much restricted British aviation industry of today represents a buoyant oasis in the country's industrial wasteland and as such is a powerful force in Britain's economic life.

'Working for Britain's future prosperity' was how British Aerospace described itself in the early nineteen eighties. It is a reasonable question to ask how much greater would that future prosperity be if, in the space of a decade beginning in the mid-nineteen fifties, this advanced technology and potentially high profit industry, in which Britain was pre-eminent, had not been laid waste by a combination of lack of conviction, constancy and direction.

Just how such a monstrous hash could have been made of so favourable an initial situation is a question which has been both exercising the minds and challenging the understanding of expert commentators for years. Their conclusions have been extensively argued in print, not least by Charles Gardner in *British Aircraft Corporation*, Stephen Hastings in *The Murder of the TSR-2*, Arthur Reed in *Britain's Aircraft Industry* and Derek Wood in *Project Cancelled*. The burden of some of their forcefully expressed arguments, which are set against a background of what one of them in righteous anger described as 'intrigue, prejudice and incompetence', can be distilled into the following assertions.

There had always been a distinct lack of positive commitment to the aircraft industry and a clear and consistent view of what it was expected to achieve on the part of successive British governments which were, of course, its major customer and patron. The industry's fortunes were of necessity linked to the prevailing attitudes, strategic concepts and whims of the current government, not to mention the exigencies it faced, including a need for financial restraint. Such financial restraint was often linked to the timorousness of governments when faced with financing necessarily expensive advanced technology projects. Not unconnected to this is the fact that aircraft manufacture owes its existence largely to, and derives some of its greatest advances from, the military application of aeronautics, a potentially inhibiting factor in times of peace.

All this was exacerbated by the peculiarities of the British system in which government ministers are drawn from the ranks of professional politicians who are in turn advised by civil servants with a classical education. When it comes to understanding the complexities and implications of advanced technology projects most experts agree that such men as these are at a clear disadvantage. One civil service department in particular, the Treasury, has been cited in its employment of obstructionist tactics as being the probable principal brake on Britain's technological advance. In other countries civil servants tend to be more technocratic than in Britain. In France, for example, large numbers of them are products of the country's élite technological university, the École Polytechnique.

Added to this is the vexed question of the American connection. One strongly held view is that it has been the policy of the United States to impose a complete American monopoly in aerospace on the West in order to finance the US space programme and put the American aircraft industry in an unassailable position. Competitors were to be reduced to what one commentator called 'technical helots' confined to the manufacture of low-technology products or to the role of sub-contractor to the Americans. To accomplish this the British aircraft industry had to be broken and the process is said to have begun as long ago as the mid-nineteen fifties.

It was a process facilitated by the continuing close links established between Britain and America during World War II through which British officials were subjected to prolonged exposure to American salesmanship. This was compounded by the notion that to duplicate the

American effort was both unnecessary and futile, particularly in the face of United States omnipotence with which British officials and politicians allowed themselves to be unduly overawed. British officials and politicians also appear to have been mesmerized by what they saw as American omniscience. The idea picked up in the United States that the manned military aircraft was obsolete, so slavishly acted upon in Britain in 1957 with disastrous results, was just one example of this.

And the process continues. In 1981 when the British aircraft industry was on the threshold of something of a renaissance the survey *The British Defence Industry* still saw making bits and pieces under subcontract for the Americans as a favoured area for British firms. In 1986 Westland, the near-bankrupt company into which all British helicopter production is now concentrated, was sold off to the Americans with the connivance of the British government after the most blatant example of political chicanery of modern times. The uproar which followed led to the resignation of two senior cabinet ministers. It was a fiasco at one with the continuing grim saga of British advanced technology since World War II.

Later an all-party defence committee of MPs concluded that Britain's interests had not been best served by selling off a public company important to the nation's defence interests to a country whose own defence equipment market is protected from foreign competition and foreign ownership. Indeed it was widely argued that a revival of British helicopter development and production was most certainly not in the long-term interests of Westland's American purchaser.

It is a view that would undoubtedly have been shared by one of Britain's most outstanding aeronautical engineers, the late Sir Barnes Wallis, and with good reason. In 1953 Sir Barnes, designer of the R100 airship and the Wellington bomber and inventor of the bouncing bomb, had patented his variable geometry or swing-wing which could give an aircraft a unique capacity for both cruising at very low speeds and supersonic flight. After the now infamous Defence White Paper of 1957 British government support for the swing-wing concept was withdrawn. The Americans were then given all the Wallis data. Not only did they use it in a manner that was not acceptable to him but also the expected financial support from the Americans for a British swing-wing programme in exchange for the data was not forthcoming. It is perhaps hardly surprising therefore that Sir Barnes Wallis was one of the most vociferous critics of the conclusion that Britain should be content with the role of technological appendage of the United States. Sir Barnes' view of the outcome of such a policy, voiced as long ago as 1965, was positively apocalyptic: 'Not the strength, not even the weakness, but the death of England would follow.'

Supreme on Water, Land and in the Air

One outcrop of Britain's spectacular aeronautical advance of the nineteen fifties was the country's pioneering role in the application of the jet or gas-turbine engine to a variety of uses other than powering aircraft. In 1952 the world's first standby gas-turbine electricity generator came into operation in Manchester and a British merchant vessel became the first ship to be propelled by a gas turbine. The gas-turbine engine had already made motoring history two years earlier in March 1950 when the Rover Car Company's celebrated jet car, the world's first, had been put through its paces at Silverstone. The car's registration number was appropriately JET 1. In its invention and utilization the jet engine was without doubt an example *par excellence* of the British propensity for radical new ideas and innovative approaches when it came to truly advanced technology.

Regrettably, despite the pioneering work with Rover's JET 1 and its experimental successors in the sixties, Britain would ultimately abandon work on this particular application of the jet engine. She went on, however, to establish herself as a prime supplier of gas-turbine engines for other non-aeronautical uses. By the mid-nineteen eighties the ships of no fewer than twenty-five of the world's navies were powered by such engines, all, of course, originally developed for aircraft. Japan, West Germany and others may between them have put paid to Britain's position as the world's leading ship builder but the ships built in their yards would as likely as not be fitted with British gas-turbine engines. The same was true of gas-turbine generators. Britain was also in the forefront when it came to the application of the gas turbine to pumping oil and gas. It is therefore hardly surprising that 1984 saw the delivery for industrial use of the 1000th Rolls-Royce Avon engine that had powered so many of Britain's successful, record-breaking jet aircraft of the fifties decade.

A veritable host of world records was another outcrop of Britain's advance in aeronautics in the fifties. There was, for example, the world air speed record and the world altitude record for a manned aircraft, not to mention the rate-of-climb, distance and innumerable point-to-point records which British aircraft broke with almost monotonous regularity during the decade as aviation, assisted by British ingenuity, made vast strides.

Simultaneous with the world air speed record Britain also held the world land speed record and the world water speed record. This last record also underscored Britain's world supremacy in aeronautics as Donald Campbell's record-breaking boat *Bluebird* was powered by a British aircraft engine developed for the world's first jet flying boat. And in the sixties Campbell would keep the land speed record in British hands in his car *Bluebird* driven by an engine used in the Britannia airliner.

Not that Britain's possession of the world speed triple crown was considered in any way remarkable at the time. After all, the world land and water speed records had, since the early twenties and early thirties respectively, been almost permanent British possessions, to which the world air speed record had not infrequently been added. As with most other fields of human endeavour, if there were records to be broken then Britain was expected to be in the vanguard of those nations which broke them. In the nineteen fifties it seemed that it had always been like that and probably always would be.

These achievements were naturally a compelling proclamation of British expertise and, in the case of those related to aeronautics, an invaluable shop window for the products they were intended to advertise. And by keeping Britain in the world's focus they would also have played a significant part in indirectly promoting a myriad unrelated British products of which Britain was a major, or even the principal, manufacturer.

Britain would subsequently lose the world air, water and land speed records. When, however, the land speed record was wrested back for Britain in 1983 by Richard Noble in his jet car *Thrust 2* it was with the application of nineteen fifties British aircraft technology. The vehicle was powered by a Rolls-Royce Avon engine taken from a Lightning supersonic fighter.

Britain may yet hold both the world land and water speed records some time in the future. It is, however, unlikely that an all-British aircraft will ever again hold the world air speed or altitude records as these can only be held by those countries that are independently in the vanguard of aeronautical technology, which Britain undoubtedly was in the nineteen fifties but is no more.

3

MISSILES AND SPACE

Rockets Galore

In addition to aircraft a large part of the British aeronautical industry's efforts during the nineteen fifties was
devoted to various types of guided missiles. One little
known fact is that the world's first guided missile was
British. Developed during World War I, and largely the
work of the renowned physicist Professor A. M. Low, this
was a scaled-down radio-controlled aircraft carrying an
explosive charge. But the modern concept of the guided
missile propelled by a rocket engine dates from the close
of World War II.

So far as rocketry is concerned, it was Sir William
Congreve who, in the early nineteenth century, was
responsible for the successful, but short lived, revival of
the war rocket after this weapon's long eclipse in Europe.
His inspiration came from a campaign in India during the
previous century in which the British were badly mauled
by a native army equipped with rockets. The British went
on to use rockets to some effect in the Napoleonic wars
and against the United States in the American war of

1812, a fact recorded for posterity in the American national anthem by the lines referring to the 'rocket's red glare' and 'bombs bursting in the air'. And it was the British who were the first to use modern rockets as weapons of war, which they did against the Germans after the loss of much of their conventional artillery at Dunkirk in the late Spring of 1940.

By the early nineteen fifties it was well recognized that the guided missile, as developed from the rocket by the end of World War II, would eventually become one of the decisive instruments of war, whether at sea, on land or in the air. Some indication of Britain's progress in this particular field can be gained from an offer made to her in 1952 to use American facilities to test the first British atomic bomb. What prompted this offer was not altruism but the fact that the British atomic artillery and guided missile programme was going better than that of the United States and the Americans hoped to gain access to British technology in return for their 'generosity'. As it happened the offer was declined.

Britain's principal testing site for her missile technology was at Woomera in Australia. A joint British and Australian endeavour, Woomera, at three thousand miles in length, was the longest land missile range outside the USSR. As well as the erection of launching pads and the like the project involved building an entire town with all modern amenities in the heart of the inhospitable Australian bush to house scientists, technicians and their families. It also involved providing a research facility and laboratory complex at Salisbury, near Adelaide, as well as maintaining a constant ferry service to convey men and materials from Britain to Australia, a distance of 12,000 miles.

By the end of the fifties decade Woomera had established itself as the best equipped, best managed and most cost-effective range in the whole of the western world. Because of this and its position on the Earth's surface the Americans not only installed equipment of their own there but also carried out experiments using *British* research rockets.

One of the outstanding spin-off benefits to accrue to Britain as a result of missile testing at Woomera was WREDAC (Weapons Research Establishment Digital Automatic Computer) which revolutionized the science of data reduction and attracted world attention. Subsequently similar instruments throughout the West would be based on this pattern.

Over 400 companies employing several thousand scientific and engineering staff were engaged in Britain's missile activity. They would provide the country with an impressive range of products that immediately found markets overseas, like the Bloodhound anti-aircraft missile and the Seaslug, which would be adopted by no fewer than fifteen of the world's navies.

For Britain's exclusive use was the Blue Steel stand-off bomb to be carried by the Vulcan and Victor V-bombers. This powerful nuclear flying-bomb, or strategic stand-off missile, would be released when the aircraft carrying it was about 200 miles from the bomb's ultimate destination, allowing the actual bomber to 'stand off' from the target and not have to penetrate the enemy's ring of defences.

Britain also had Skylark and Black Knight. Skylark was a 25 feet long research rocket for use in upper atmosphere experiments at heights of up to 150 miles. Black Knight, on the other hand, was rather bigger and more sophisticated. An experimental rocket, it was capable of reaching a height in excess of 500 miles, a height greater than that achieved by any other known single-stage rocket of the late fifties and early sixties.

The purpose of Black Knight was to be a test bed for an undertaking of far greater magnitude, work on which had started, like that on Black Knight, in 1954. This was Britain's massive ballistic missile Blue Streak. 'The size of a railway carriage', it was based on the American Atlas intercontinental ballistic missile (the result of a technology exchange agreement between Britain and the United States) and designed to carry a thermonuclear, or H-bomb, warhead over a distance of 2500 miles, following a trajectory that would transport it 620 miles into space. It was intended that Blue Streak should succeed the V-bombers and their Blue Steel stand-off missiles as the principal delivery system for Britain's strategic nuclear deterrent some time in the nineteen sixties.

Blue Streak's military role was officially confirmed in 1959 and the first test firing was scheduled for 1960. Also in 1959 the government announced that there would be an immediate start to Britain's own space programme in which Blue Streak, Black Knight and other British missiles might play a part.

The space age was considered to have begun some two years earlier in October 1957 when the Soviet Union placed the world's first artificial satellite into orbit 560 miles above the Earth (a height achieved by Britain's Black Knight rocket a year later). In January 1958 the Americans rather hastily orbited their first satellite but it was miniscule by Russian standards.

That Britain too should embark on a major space programme was deemed the utmost necessity. As the *Times* succinctly put it:

> The question remains whether a nation which depends increasingly for its livelihood on exporting an ever more technical range of products can afford to appear in the eyes of the world as a back number in what may well be for years ahead the most spectacular field of scientific exploration and development.

And, of course, Britain possessed the technology for such an enterprise. Not only could a combination of Blue Streak and Black Knight put satellites into Earth orbit but Blue Streak was also capable of providing the main booster for Venus and Mars flights and manned orbital flights like its 'sister' the American Atlas. Indeed, the projected date for the first British manned orbital space-flight was 1965, the year of America's first multiple (two-man) orbital spaceflight.

All of which would have been a practical extension to the impressive theoretical contribution which English-men had already made in this particular field, from Sir Isaac Newton in the seventeenth century to the twentieth century scientist and world renowned science fiction writer Arthur C. Clarke, whose brain-child was the com-munications satellite.

Arthur C. Clarke was a member of the British Inter-planetary Society, which by the nineteen fifties had established itself as one of the world's leading research bodies dealing with the theoretical problems of space travel and the utilization of space generally. As early as 1939 the BIS had designed a spaceship to travel to the moon and back. So advanced was the scheme that it bore a striking resemblance to the Apollo moon landing pro-ject of thirty years later. The BIS was also responsible for a plan to put a Briton in space with an adapted German V-2 rocket in the late nineteen forties, more than a decade in advance of the first Russian and American spacemen. Unfortunately the British government was unable to comprehend the significance of such an enterprise and so nothing came of it.

British achievement was in evidence, too, in the related area of radio astronomy, the gathering and investigation of radio waves from the stars. Indeed, it was a field in which Britain was predominant. This was exemplified by the completion in 1957 of two new radio telescopes. The first of these, at Jodrell Bank, came into operation just in time to track the first Russian satellites and quickly established itself on both sides of the Iron Curtain as an unrivalled centre for space-tracking and communica-tions. The second radio telescope was at Cambridge. The two were completely different in design but each was the biggest of its kind in the world. In 1958 World Data Centre 'C' was established at Slough, the purpose of which was to collect information on satellites and other space activity and exchange it with the two other World Data Centres, 'A' in Washington and 'B' in Moscow.

The full details of Britain's space programme were finally announced by the Macmillan government late in 1959. They were unbelievable. It had been decided that there would be no major British space programme based on Britain's ballistic missile, Blue Streak, and experimental rocket, Black Knight, nor even the most acceptable alternative, a British Commonwealth effort. Instead Britain would have to confine herself solely to international space ventures, beginning with a most junior of junior partnership with the United States in which small British scientific satellites would be launched by American rockets at a cost of a couple of hundred thousand pounds.

And this was the only other country besides America and Russia to possess the necessary technology for space exploration and was already the biggest participant in space activity outside the United States and the Soviet Union. Britain was a space superpower, no less, for whom a major independent space programme was widely seen as crucial to economic survival.

The development costs of such a programme, involving a two or three-man spaceflight project, were calculated in 1959 at about the same as those for a jet airliner. As at that time Britain already had a number of jet airliners either in production or at the development stage it would seem that such a space programme was far from being an economic impossibility. But then, the death-knell of Britain as an independent aircraft producer had already been tolled through the same inadequacies in Britain's decision makers that now denied the country a place among the stars.

'The Grossest Folly'

In April 1960 Blue Streak was cancelled as a military weapon in favour of an American-supplied nuclear delivery system. As the government had set its face against such an enterprise there was, of course, no question of Blue Streak continuing to be developed as part of a major British space effort. 'No country in the world – neither America nor Russia – is rich enough or powerful enough to direct its manpower to producing a rocket solely for the purpose of space research', said Minister for Science Lord Hailsham. His Lordship could not have been more wrong.

Blue Streak was destined to become part of a spectacularly unsuccessful European space programme in which the only thing that worked was Blue Streak. The project finally sank in a sea of Euro-recrimination in 1972 and so died Blue Streak, still at that time the largest rocket developed outside the Soviet Union and the United States. With the demise of Blue Streak direct contact between British scientists and technicians and rocket technology on a respectable scale came to an end.

Although British space activity, such as it was, remained largely confined to international co-operative ventures, as adumbrated by the Macmillan government in 1959, the country did indulge itself in one small wholly national effort. This was an attempt to enlarge the highly successful Black Knight experimental rocket into a three-stage vehicle which would place satellites, chiefly in the communications field and weighing only a couple of hundred pounds, into orbit. Work on the project, named Black Arrow, began in 1965. It was designed to give Britain 'a distinctive capability in space' and as such was one genuine advanced technology project that *did* evolve from the Wilson government's 'white hot technological revolution'.

Black Arrow eventually placed a 145 lb satellite called Prospero into orbit from Woomera in October 1971. But the launching rated very little media coverage. The days when Britons regarded anything their country did as being in any way significant were long since past. It was, in any case, not much of an achievement by 1971 standards. After all France, which although a member of the failed European space project pursued a space programme of her own, had put a small satellite into orbit as early as 1965, the projected year for a British manned orbital flight had work begun in 1959 on adapting Blue Streak for space research. Japan and China followed suit in 1970, making them the fourth and fifth members of the exclusive club of 'cosmic powers' after Russia, America and France.

If nothing else Black Arrow served to illustrate just how far Britain had fallen behind in space capability since the nineteen fifties when she measured herself technologically in relation to the two superpowers. With an annual budget of a mere £3m and a planned launch rate of only one rocket per year this ludicrously belated attempt to give Britain space capability was in any case largely irrelevant. But at least it meant that the British were able to accomplish on their own what they failed to achieve in partnership with the Europeans.

It was to be a short-lived accomplishment. The Heath government, which inherited the Black Arrow project in 1970, decreed even before it had taken place that the first launching by Black Arrow would also be the last and that the country should revert to its reliance on the United States for the launching of British satellites. An independent space venture would not be countenanced. Thus Britain became the first, and so far only, member of the cosmic club to resign its membership.

By comparison others have strengthened their right to membership. In 1973, after the failure of the original European space effort, a new venture was set on foot under the auspices of the European Space Agency (ESA). This was the Ariane launcher project, another attempt to give Europe a credible independent space capability and break the grip of the American monopoly. This had been regarded as absolutely vital by France in particular ever since the late nineteen sixties when the Americans refused to launch one of her telecommunications satellites without a guarantee that its use would be restricted.

The Ariane launcher was, and still is, built by some fifty firms in ten countries, with manufacturers receiving orders for equipment in due proportion to their country's financial stake in the enterprise, which in Britain's case is a miniscule 3.73 per cent. Nevertheless Ariane is essentially a French project. Not only is Ariane assembled in France but most of its technology is French and France provides two thirds of the budget as well as the launch facilities in French Guyana. It is really a case of foreign countries joining a major French space effort. As such it is a classic example, if ever there was one, of the French tendency, unlike that of the British, to enter fully into international collaborative agreements only from a position of strength. To the French, space, like all their other advanced technological pursuits, is intrinsically linked to the independence and greatness of France and the nation's destiny. France is, in any case, the only true space (and ballistic missile) nation in Europe and her industries have benefited greatly from the consequent technological fertilization.

So successful had the Ariane launcher become by the nineteen eighties that clients with satellites to be put into orbit, including some from the United States, were actually taking their custom away from the American Space Shuttle and giving it to Ariane. After the Space Shuttle disaster in 1986 Ariane would net 50 per cent of all launcher activity, which has now become a multi-billion dollar business.

Also moving towards joining the satellite launching bonanza is Japan where, commercial considerations apart, it is feared that without an independent launcher the Japanese will not be taken seriously in the

Britain inaugurated the age of jet travel in May 1952 when the Comet 1 became the first jet airliner in the world to enter passenger service. But there was a price to pay for being ahead of the field.

Sublime studies in symmetry and power and a striking manifestation of Britain's military aeronautical supremacy in the fifties decade, the unique V-bombers, the Vulcan (*bottom*) leading the Valiant and the Victor, all of which broke entirely new ground in aerodynamics.

VICKERS 1000
Four Rolls-Royce Conway By-Pass Jet Engines

Britain's considerable lead in civil aviation was to be maintained by the V1000/VC7 which would have been the world's first long-haul big jet transport. The project was, however, cancelled in 1955, leaving the field wide open to the Americans.

The incredible Fairey Delta 2 'Flying Dart', one of a number of advanced British military aircraft of revolutionary design cancelled in 1957. Another blow from which the British aircraft industry would never recover.

Perhaps the most promising item in Britain's ambitious helicopter programme of the nineteen fifties was the Rotodyne, a hybrid airliner/helicopter which was in effect the world's first vertical take-off and landing transport. Although it generated intense interest at home and abroad the project was abandoned, as eventually was all wholly British helicopter development.

The TSR2 (Tactical Strike and Reconnaissance Aircraft) represented the apogee of those skills and expertise of the British aircraft industry that had burgeoned in the fifties decade. Its cancellation in 1965 signalled the end of Britain as an independent manufacturer of truly advanced military aircraft.

The versatile Harrier jump jet taking off from the coalyard at St Pancras railway station, London. The jump jet was one of the most outstanding examples of Britain's pioneering role in revolutionary aeronautical technique; and it was to be the last. Britain would effectively hand over future development of this, her own invention, to the United States.

The British experimental rocket Black Knight. First launched in 1958 it was capable of reaching a height in excess of 500 miles, a height greater than that achieved by any other known single-stage rocket.

Britain's ballistic missile Blue Streak was the proposed launcher for a major British space programme in the late nineteen fifties. Nevertheless, Britain would ultimately become the only country so far both to possess and then abandon a ballistic missile and to resign from the exclusive club of cosmic powers.

Britain acquired the hydrogen bomb in May 1957. But almost immediately afterwards steps were taken which would lead to the demise of the genuinely independent all-British deterrent and to nuclear (and therefore political) dependence on the United States.

Britain established a clear world lead in the exploitation of atomic power to generate electricity with the commissioning, in 1956, of the first large-scale nuclear power station at Calder Hall. Ironically a generation later Britain would find herself dependent on American hand-me-down technology for her nuclear energy programme.

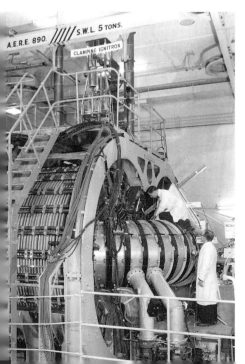

ZETA (Zero Energy Thermonuclear Assembly) at Harwell was the world's biggest research apparatus devoted to harnessing the power that had produced the hydrogen bomb and in 1957 had come closest to achieving the, as yet still elusive, desired results. Britain's thermo-nuclear energy programme has since been largely absorbed into an international project.

In 1952 Britain became the world's chief exporter of radioactive isotopes. Most of them emanated from BEPO (British Experimental Pile Operation) at Harwell. This activity remains one of the successful outcrops left over from the country's dazzling display of nuclear ingenuity of a generation ago.

international meetings to thrash out the rules for the peaceful use of space. Japan also sees space research as a vital tool with which to maintain her competitiveness in high-technology, such as computers. She expects to become a major space nation by the nineteen nineties with hardware equal to anything in Europe and America and has longer term plans for a manned space programme to colonize the moon and the planets.

Meanwhile 'technologically backward' China has already received contracts for launching the satellites of other nations, having progressed to putting animals into space and entered the early stages of developing manned spacecraft and skylabs. To the Chinese government space technology is a vital element in China's overall modernization. Likewise 'Third World' India's independent launcher, which put its first satellite into orbit in 1980, is regarded as a proud symbol of the country's new thrusting image. Brazil too is reportedly well on the way to becoming a space power.

Tiny Israel launched her first satellite in 1988. The principal motivation behind the project is believed to have been dissatisfaction with American-supplied satellite intelligence. 'If you are fed from the crumbs of others according to their moods this is very inconvenient and very difficult', said the chief of Israel's General Satellite Corporation. 'If you have your own independent capability you climb one level higher.' But military considerations apart, as the Israeli prime minister rightly pointed out: 'It puts Israel into the upper echelon among modern technological nations.'

Space has, of course, already revolutionized whole areas of science and technology from telecommunications to making the computer a fact of everyday life. And the absence of gravity is expected to make possible the production of new materials and medicines in space factories and laboratories. Indeed, space research is where most major technological breakthroughs are expected to emanate from in the future, with nations which are not involved left far behind. This is why the governments of so many countries, large and small, rich and poor, see the commercial exploitation of space as the source of tomorrow's prosperity and therefore one of the principal areas on which they should focus.

So confident of this is the Soviet government that it is said to have evolved a master plan to develop space as a wealth-creating resource calculated to give the Soviet Union the economic leadership of the world and the Russian people the highest standard of living on Earth. While the Americans, also mindful of the importance of space in the exercise of global economic as well as political influence, announced a revitalized national space programme early in 1988, the object of which was to maintain the United States in her position as the world's top nation.

The opportunities offered by space technology are clearly limitless and its relevance to a country's economy and security, as well as its scientific and political interests, incalculable. Indeed, it is something in which no modern technological nation worthy of the description can afford not to make a substantial investment. Nevertheless the space horizons of successive British governments have remained far from limitless, an attitude which is exemplified by their expenditure on space. This, in direct contrast to other countries, has actually been halved in real terms since the mid-nineteen seventies. In fact, when it comes to levels of public non-military expenditure on space Britain is at the bottom of the league table of advanced industrial nations, a position which reflects exactly her standing as an industrialized power. In 1987 contingency funds were needed to avoid Britain's eviction from the European Space Agency, while the director-general of the fledgling British National Space Centre resigned because of the government's refusal to increase the country's derisory space funding to a figure that was still modest by other nations' standards. Finally, the British government became the only member of the European Space Agency not to back a massive new French inspired ESA initiative designed to give Europe a considerably enhanced capability in space by the year 2000. In the view of a veritable chorus of critics this would effectively cut the country off from the technologies of the twenty-first century. For the British government to ignore space in this way was seen as tantamount to the Elizabethans turning their backs on the New World or the Victorians refusing to build railways.

The government's attitude is particularly surprising when viewed in the light of the substantial benefits which Britain has already derived from space, partly as a legatee of earlier, greater involvement. British companies, for instance, have established a world lead in the highly lucrative, albeit pedestrian, field of processing data from satellites employed in meteorology, mapping, mineral prospecting and surveillance. Britain is also very much involved in the booming communications satellite business. Indeed, a large percentage of the communications satellites now in orbit are of British design, although they are not necessarily of wholly British manufacture. Even so, it is an area of advanced technology spin-off activity which was expanding at a time when many of the country's more traditional industries had either stagnated or were in decline. There are, too, the technical contributions to Ariane and multinational scientific and experimental spacecraft, as well as other collaborative and sub-contract work, especially with and for the Americans, although this brings with it the all too familiar worrying implications of reliance on the United States. Finally, but by no means least, is the considerable knowledge and world-wide prestige which have accrued to Britain over the years from the significant discoveries made by her own scientific satellites. On all of this, and more, the British government would appear to be turning its back.

Nevertheless British scientists continue to beaver away on what is in effect a space mission to nowhere. The fruits of their labours include the revolutionary 18,000 mph British HOTOL (horizontal take-off and landing) space-plane designed to travel into space and back again using normal runways like a conventional aircraft. It is esti-mated that HOTOL could put payloads into orbit at about one fifth the cost of the comparatively crude launchers in current use. It could also carry passengers from Britain to Australia in 45 minutes. But in 1988 the British govern-ment, in keeping with its attitude to space generally, withdrew its financial support from the project (thereby, it was said, reducing Britain's space commitment to the level of Belgium and Spain) and insisted that for its future development HOTOL must find foreign backers. The decision provoked the now all too familiar, and of course unheeded, uproar as once again Britain looked like losing control of a brilliant aerospace project; one that could give the country a substantial world lead in space technology.

Not that there had ever been any question of Britain going it *entirely* alone in any case. Collaboration of one sort or another was always regarded as the only means whereby HOTOL could eventually come to fruition, per-haps through the European Space Agency or with Japan or the United States. The Americans had already cast envious eyes over this British breakthrough, anxious to learn its secrets. To even hint that Britain should operate independently at the leading edge of technology as she did a generation ago (and other nations still do) rather than totally in co-operation with others is now con-sidered a heresy of the darkest hue.

As it is, no spacecraft, apart from Prospero in 1971, has ever been launched by anything originating in Britain. British scientific satellites of the nineteen sixties and seventies, for example, were put into space by the American Scout launch vehicle, known appropriately as the 'poor man's rocket', in accordance with the modest Anglo-American space programme agreed to in 1959.

The nearest thing to a space launcher now left to the British aerospace industry is the Skylark sounding rocket. This has been used by a number of countries in upper atmosphere experiments since its first launch in 1956 and has, since that time, made an enormous contribution to the knowledge of astronomy, but it cannot put anything into orbit. Other than that British rocket activity is essentially restricted to the production of short-range tactical missiles. Consequently facilities as grand as those at Woomera are no longer required. Britain's interest in the range in fact ended in 1980 after thirty-four years, an event which received virtually no media coverage.

The tactical missile pool, to which Britain is now largely confined, is not exactly exclusive as a number of countries, some quite small, are large fish in its fairly crowded waters. France, naturally, is well represented by a missile industry that was practically non-existent in the nineteen fifties but which is now technologically on a par with that of the United States and includes ballistic missiles and space launchers in its list of products. It was, of course, the French who produced the Exocet missile which had such a devastating effect on the British Falklands task force in 1982.

At about that time British Aerospace was claiming it manufactured 'a larger range of tactical missiles than any other country in the western world'. A large claim indeed considering the Falklands task force was heavily reliant on American-supplied tactical guided missiles. And it was the threat of a direct hit on the Argentine headquarters in Port Stanley by one of these, the Pavestrike laser-guided 'smart' bomb, that is said to have been instrumental in persuading General Menendez to surrender his forces.

Even so, as with other branches of the aerospace industry, missile manufacturing has become important both to the nation's defence and to the economy. But because it is a much restricted activity there is little to keep British scientists and technicians at home. They simply take their talents overseas. This was the complaint made to the House of Commons Defence Committee in 1980 by Admiral Sir Raymond Lygo, chairman of the missile division of British Aerospace. 'Half of southern California is populated with my expatriates as far as I can see', bemoaned the admiral. 'That is where they go. They do not go off to the Balls Pond Road pen factory and make Biros.'

The restrictions imposed on Britain's space activity have had the same effect. As long ago as 1959 the government was warned that if nothing was done offici- ally to stimulate space research in Britain and the Com- monwealth those sufficiently gifted and interested would automatically gravitate to where there was space activity. Well nothing was done officially to stimulate space research in Britain and the Commonwealth on any reasonable scale. Those sufficiently gifted and interested did gravitate to where there was space activity, to the United States National Aeronautics and Space Adminis- tration spaceflight centres to be precise, where many British and Commonwealth scientists not only made outstanding contributions to the American space effort but also attained positions of power and influence.

This was highlighted by a statement made by Prime Minister Margaret Thatcher in 1983: 'When I first went over to NASA, the US space agency, years ago, in the middle sixties, the person there in charge of, I believe, the Gemini programme was a person from my own consti- tuency.' To this display of misplaced pride was added what can only be interpreted as a complete lack of understanding of what was required to rectify the matter: 'So we *have* the scientific genius, the inventive genius, but we haven't got enough of the *enterprise* to turn it into profit.' What was really required was, of course, a government sponsored major British space programme instead of a disperate dabbling of toes in the shallows of other peoples cosmic pools.

As it is, not only did the American space effort benefit from 'the scientific genius, the inventive genius' of the British but the British could also be said to have played a large part in financing it. By leaving the United States a clear field in the jet transport business from the late fifties onwards, after leading the way earlier in the decade, and by buying American jet airliners, Britain contributed substantially to America's balance of payments, which in turn made a large-scale US space programme possible.

The most outstanding single British contribution to the American space effort was not, however, made by a Briton brain-drained to NASA. It was made by Francis Bacon, a descendant of the seventeenth century philosopher and statesman, and involved his revolutionary fuel cell or 'magic battery' which converts chemical power into electricity. Such was the magnitude of Bacon's contribution that without his invention, which had entailed twenty years of grinding struggle to bring it to fruition, the Americans could never have put a man on the moon. So the great leap for mankind and the planting of the Stars and Stripes on the moon's surface in July 1969 was as much a *British* accomplishment as it was American.

Describing British brains and ingenuity as the country's greatest natural resource is a common practice among politicians. Common also is their call for a more technologically-minded Britain. But their own record in harnessing this natural resource and in understanding what is required to bring about the desired result is, as we have seen, quite abysmal. And the situation is apparently a never changing one. While in America in 1981 Margaret Thatcher visited the Goddard Spaceflight Centre near Washington. The purpose of the visit was to promote British initiative and inspect projects in which Britain

47

was involved. 'It's real. It's real. This is it, it's real. It's not imagination, it's real . . . it's actually up there', she trilled as her eyes fell on the display of space hardware. To the rest of mankind the space age was already a quarter of a century old; it had actually been 'up there' that long. And it was in large part due to the Conservative government's decision in 1959, the year Thatcher entered Parliament, that Britain was not 'up there', under her own steam as it were, with all the other space powers.

In that fateful year, when a full-scale British space programme was being debated and Britain possessed the technology for such an enterprise on a superpower scale, the government was warned by its Advisory Council on Scientific Policy, not one of whose members was involved in space research, that 'to shoulder the crippling cost of a large programme of space exploration on a purely national basis would be . . . the grossest folly'. This was regarded at the time by genuine experts as arrant nonsense; history would prove them right. The 'grossest folly' has in fact turned out to be that Britain did *not* engage in a large programme of space exploration. As a prominent figure in the British Interplanetary Society, Maurice Allward, prophesied in the Society's journal *Spaceflight* as far back as July 1957:

> The nation with an efficient intercontinental ballistic missile has the first stepping stone to the planets. So great a prize must not be allowed to slip through Britain's fingers. If it does the adverse effects on our future history will be with us not for years, but centuries.

4

NUCLEAR POWER

'Overwhelming Nuclear Retaliation'

Blue Streak, the cornerstone of the hoped for large-scale all-British space programme of a generation ago, was developed in the first instance as a ballistic missile to carry Britain's nuclear deterrent. As such it represented an attempt to keep pace, insofar as Britain's resources would allow, with the United States and the Soviet Union in the development of nuclear power for weapons of war.

As with so much else Britain was very much in the vanguard of the nuclear revolution. The country's outstanding early pioneering work in this field is fairly widely appreciated. What is probably less well known is that the British were the first to begin work on an atomic bomb. This was in 1941 during Britain's darkest hour. 'No nation', it had been decided, 'would care to risk being caught without a weapon of such decisive possibilities.'

Inspired by Britain's example the Americans began to develop a bomb of their own. They also proposed that the British should join them in a combined nuclear effort. The offer was refused. Britain did not wish to be at the mercy of the United States and in any case she was ahead of America in nuclear research in those early years and was also progressing at a faster rate.

The British, however, subsequently changed their mind. In 1943 they agreed to absorb their effort into the now larger and more rapidly developing nuclear programme of the United States while it was still possible for Britain to make a substantial contribution to a joint project and at the same time benefit from American advances. It should be said, however, that the Anglo-American nuclear partnership was not exactly lacking in acrimony and mutual suspicion.

Thus Great Britain became the co-producer of the world's first atomic bomb, developed under the code-name Manhattan Project and tested in New Mexico in July 1945. The following month atomic bombs were dropped on Hiroshima and Nagasaki in Japan by the United States Air Force, so precipitating the end of World War II.

Later it would be admitted that without the British this means of putting a period to a long and costly war would not have been available to the Americans. But at the time the United States took what was thought of in the British camp as too much credit for the enterprise. So great was this feeling that the then British prime minister, Clement Attlee, was compelled to issue a statement pointing out in the tersest of terms just how significant the British and Canadian contribution had been. (Canada had played a vital role in both the initial British and the later Anglo-American nuclear programmes.)

Britain's contribution to the Manhattan Project, as well as two wartime agreements and assurances given in November 1945 by the American president, Harry Truman, led to the expectation in Britain that the Anglo-American nuclear partnership would continue after the war. The United States government, though, had become conscious of its nuclear monopoly and was anxious to maintain it. And so, earlier co-operation, agreements and assurances notwithstanding, the door was unceremoniously slammed on further exchanges of nuclear information between Britain (and any other country for that matter) and the United States by the passing of the McMahon Act by the American Senate in August 1946. The Americans claimed their action was in the interests of world peace. British Prime Minister Clement Attlee saw things differently. He believed 'the Senate wanted to have everything for America'.

But Britain held an ace card marked with something that is indispensable to nuclear technology, uranium. Not only had Britain managed to tie up much of the Earth's ore deposits but she also effectively controlled world production of this valuable element. In recognition of this some very limited information on nuclear matters, although nothing relating to military weapons, was imparted by the United States. It has been suggested that Britain may conceivably have obtained far more information of benefit to a British nuclear programme had she fully exploited her virtual monopoly of vital raw materials. Her failure to do so has been much remarked upon, not least by the Americans themselves.

It goes without saying that the McMahon Act was viewed by America's cast-off nuclear partners, Britain and Canada, as an act of betrayal. The fury and resentment it engendered is said to linger within the British and Canadian nuclear establishments to this very day.

This resentment may well have been the reason why scientists in Britain were expressly forbidden to pass on information to the Americans concerning an audacious early postwar British project, the implications of which were arguably as great as the nuclear bomb. The project involved an attempt to develop a charged particle beam weapon, which was in effect that essential science fiction artefact, the ray gun. But British scientists were thwarted in their efforts because they could not generate enough electrical power with the technology then available to make this 'Star Wars' weapon work. Their knowledge was, however, thought to have been leaked to the Soviet Union.

In spite of the restrictions on nuclear information imposed by the United States in 1946 there existed a strong commitment within British governmental circles to the idea that Britain should, and indeed *must*, possess atomic bombs of her own. And so in January 1947, during the Labour government of Clement Attlee, the decision was taken in secret to commence, or rather recommence, the development and production of nuclear weapons in Britain.

Nevertheless the desire for a return to those wartime days of full co-operation with America in nuclear matters remained. To this end pressure was consistently applied to the United States. This increased under Winston Churchill immediately he became Conservative prime minister at the defeat of Attlee's Labour government in October 1951. As a lever Churchill attempted to use the fact that in 1951 Britain had become an 'aircraft carrier' for United States Air Force atomic bombers, thereby making her especially vulnerable to nuclear attack, but he was sent empty away. Britain's case was not advanced by a series of breaches of security and embarrassing defections to the USSR in the late forties and early fifties. These encouraged Americans in the belief that British security standards were not up to scratch and certainly inferior to those of the United States.

On 3 October 1952 Britain detonated her first atomic bomb in the waters of the Monte Bello Islands off the north western coast of Australia. Thus Britain became the world's third nuclear power after America and Russia. (Russia had exploded her atomic bomb in 1949.)

The Americans had originally offered their test facilities for Britain's atomic bomb trials but this had been declined in favour of a Commonwealth site. In the United

States this was seen as a reflection of the resentment that the British felt at being left out in the cold with the breakup of the British/American nuclear partnership. The offer was made because the British could now provide nuclear data of value to American scientists; a remarkable situation given that Britain had restarted her nuclear programme from scratch a full eighteen months after the first 'American' atomic explosion in July 1945. Britain had become worthy of consideration and in 1954 legislation was passed in the United States which allowed for an exchange of nuclear information with Britain, although this was to be a partial exchange and not a full partnership arrangement.

Britain's quest to keep pace with America and Russia led her to the next stage in the development of nuclear weapons, the hydrogen bomb. The test-dropping of the first British H-bomb, by a Valiant V-bomber, took place on 15 May 1957 over the Christmas Island area of the Pacific Ocean. Again, it was an extraordinary achievement considering that the Americans had dropped their first transportable H-bomb barely a year earlier. (The Russians reached this stage in 1955.) Not only had Britain caught up with America in nuclear weapons development but British H-bombs were, so it would transpire, more efficient and cheaper to produce than those of the United States.

Henceforth British military forces would be organized around nuclear weapons. The threat of 'overwhelming nuclear retaliation' was seen as the only practical means of defence available to Britain. This doctrine had been worked out as early as 1951/52, before Britain had even exploded her first atomic bomb. Only later would it cross the Atlantic to become American (and NATO) policy. Thus Britain was not only the first country in the world to begin work on an atomic bomb but also the first to base its defence almost entirely on a policy of nuclear deterrence.

'Not British, Not Independent and Not a Deterrent'

Britain could knock down twelve cities in the region of Stalingrad and Moscow from bases in Britain and another dozen in the Crimea from bases in Cyprus. We did not have that power at the time of Suez. We are a major power again.

This is what Sir Winston Churchill's son, Randolph, told the American Chamber of Commerce in London on 13 November 1958. At the time Britain's first generation nuclear deterrent, the V-bomber force, was just coming on stream. But even as Randolph Churchill spoke consideration was already being given to possibilities which would ultimately lead to the demise of a truly independent all-British nuclear deterrent.

Since its inception the existence of a truly independent all-British nuclear deterrent had been widely regarded as an absolute necessity. This was the official policy of both the main political parties and it received the support of the population as a whole. Total reliance on the Americans for the defence of this small, crowded and vulnerable island was seen as unwise, even dangerous. At best it would make Britain a satellite of the United States; at worst the Americans might prove untrustworthy and abandon the British to their fate.

At the same time nuclear independence was deemed necessary for another reason: possession of the means to wage nuclear war had become the litmus paper test of great power, nay *superpower*, status. Like America and Russia, Britain had the bomb and, with the unique V-bomber force, a means of delivery. And, again like America and Russia, Britain was developing a ballistic missile, Blue Streak, as a second generation nuclear delivery system. This would keep Britain in the first rank of world powers where she felt she rightly belonged. For a nation that had been top dog for two centuries anything less was unacceptable.

Certainly it was felt that possession of nuclear weapons meant that Britain could take part in disarmament conferences with a degree of authority. An independent nuclear deterrent also, in Conservative Prime Minister Harold Macmillan's view expressed early in 1958, 'makes the United States pay greater regard to our point of view, and that is of great importance'.

Paradoxically, however, Macmillan's policy was to use Britain's nuclear independence to achieve nuclear *interdependence* with the United States. By a number of agreements beginning in July 1958 there would be a full exchange of nuclear information between Britain and America, made possible by the fact that Britain was now manifestly as advanced as, and in certain areas even more advanced than, the United States in both the military and civil applications of nuclear power. Macmillan's moves to restore harmonious relations between the two countries in the wake of the Suez debacle of 1956 provided the opportunity for this return to the wartime nuclear partnership which Britain had been pressing for since the door had been unceremoniously slammed in her face in 1946. But this 1958 revision of the McMahon Act opened up the possibility of nuclear information being exchanged between the United States and *any* ally which had made substantial progress in the field, not just Britain, although Britain was at that time the only nation to qualify.

The benefits to accrue to Britain were a reduction in the cost, coupled with an increase in the speed, of the British nuclear programme by making unnecessary the duplication of research already undertaken in the United States. But there was another consideration. Suez was supposed to have demonstrated that Britain was no longer capable of an independent world role and as a result it was felt she should channel her energies into influencing America. This fitted perfectly Harold Macmillan's ludicrous, and frequently expounded, notion that the British ought to play the part of Greeks in the new Rome that was the United States. The key which would open the doors in Washington to Britain was a special relationship based on matters nuclear.

As well as the exchange of information, Britain's V-bomber force was to be fully integrated with the American Strategic Air Command immediately the thermonuclear-equipped V-bombers began coming on stream in 1958. (It would be 1963 before the total bomber force of 180 aircraft was fully assembled.) Britain nevertheless, so it was said, retained full freedom of action in pursuing her own national security objectives.

Macmillan's policy of nuclear interdependence did not, however, receive universal approbation. It was most certainly at variance with the view of Shadow Foreign Secretary Aneurin Bevan. A militant Labour party Left-winger and former unilateral disarmer, Bevan came to see a Britain with independent nuclear capability as a potentially moderating influence on America and Russia. Macmillan's policy was also at variance with the view of the Right wing of his own Conservative party, which was, of course, at the opposite end of the political spectrum from Bevan. To the Conservative Right the United States was the enemy of British interests generally. This was exemplified by America's action over Suez when she effectively scuttled the enterprise in order, so it was believed in some quarters, to supplant Britain in the Middle East.

But under Macmillan nuclear interdependence would give way to nuclear *dependence* with the decision in April 1960 to abandon Britain's second generation nuclear deterrent, the ballistic missile Blue Streak, in favour of very much cheaper off-the-shelf delivery systems being offered by the United States to 'suitable' allies. This was something that had been under consideration since at least the Autumn of 1958. Of the American alternatives Britain chose Skybolt, a stand-off missile which would be fitted to the V-bombers.

With the purchase of the American Skybolt missile, in which deal the provision of facilities at Holy Loch in Scotland for American Polaris submarines was implicit, Britain would become totally reliant on United States technology for her second generation deterrent. In spite of government protestations to the contrary, this was widely interpreted as an abandonment of Britain's nuclear independence.

As it happened, in November 1962 the United States cancelled the Skybolt project unilaterally without prior consultation with the British. It caused the biggest crisis between Britain and America since Suez and fostered renewed demands for nuclear independence from the United States. But the outcome was completely the reverse. Under an agreement reached in December 1962 between Prime Minister Harold Macmillan and President John F. Kennedy at Nassau in the Bahamas the American submarine-based Polaris missile system was ordered to replace Skybolt.

As with Skybolt Britain would be totally reliant on the United States for the supply of the missiles, the servicing and test firing of which would have to be carried out in America. There would be no sharing of information on the actual design of the missile system with Britain. Only the vehicle which carried the weapon to its target after re-entering the Earth's atmosphere and the weapon itself were to be British. Even then Britain was dependent on the United States for weapon testing because the British test facilities in the Pacific had been abandoned. As for the Polaris submarines, these would be built in Britain under licence, with the steel for the hulls, as well as key components of the communications, navigation and guidance systems, coming from America.

In return for Polaris Britain agreed to assign her

V-bomber force, as well as the Polaris submarines when they became operational, to NATO, but with a proviso, and this was greatly stressed for the benefit of the many critics, that the British government must be in a position to resume total control over these forces if supreme national interests were at stake.

Macmillan portrayed the Nassau Agreement of 21 December 1962 as something of a coup. He had obtained the best nuclear weapons system in existence at minimum cost to Britain (research and development having already been carried out by the United States) and in so doing he declared that he had preserved the independent British nuclear deterrent within the concept of interdependence.

But by any standards the American-supplied British Polaris fleet was an eccentric definition of what constitutes an independent British nuclear deterrent and many there were, even in Macmillan's own Conservative party, who were only too eager to point this out. The same was true of the implications behind the price paid for Polaris in the commitment of the V-bomber force to the American dominated multinational North Atlantic Treaty Organization. 'I want Britain to have her own deterrent, not share one where everyone has a key in the cupboard and America has the master key', said no less a personage than the chairman of the Conservative Defence Committee, Sir Arthur Vere Harvey, in an open criticism of the Nassau Agreement.

The implication that Britain would never be allowed to use her nuclear force without American consent possessed particular cogency in the light of a pronouncement made by the US government in June 1962. 'Relatively weak national nuclear forces ... operating independently', it was said, 'are dangerous, expensive, prone to obsolescence and lacking in credibility as a deterrent.' Reference was made to 'the importance of unity and planning, concentration of executive authority and central direction. There must not be competing and conflicting strategies to meet the contingency of nuclear war.'

Clearly Britain's nuclear deterrent, which did not have the 'assured destruction' capability of that of the United States, was in the category of what the American government chose to call 'relatively weak national nuclear forces'. And this did not go unobserved in Britain. The question that it raised was whether it was likely that this same US administration would have agreed to keep the British deterrent in being with an offer of Polaris, as it did only six months later, if it meant that the British deterrent was capable of operating independently. It seems hardly surprising that some opposition Labour MPs suggested the existence of a secret protocol signed at Nassau requiring electronic locks under American control to be put in the British Polaris warheads. Certainly the Nassau Agreement seemed to smack of an *illusion* of nuclear independence for Britain, maintained with American connivance.

Under the Labour government of Harold Wilson, which came to power in October 1964, nuclear independence was no longer claimed for Britain as it had been under the Conservatives. Such an assertion was deemed to be 'fraudulent'. Polaris was, in the words of the now famous Labour election quip, 'not British, not independent and not a deterrent'.

It was under this Labour government that the Polaris submarines entered service in the late nineteen sixties as Britain's second generation nuclear deterrent. The all-British V-bomber force, which had a far greater nuclear clout than the more sophisticated American-supplied Polaris submarine fleet, was then phased out. The strategic bomber would, however, remain a vital element in the nuclear armories of the great powers. The American B-52 bomber, for instance, whose advent in the nineteen fifties was contemporaneous with the British V-bombers, is scheduled, in modified and improved form, to be part of the United States defence triad until the year 2000. This triad, which constitutes the modern credible deterrent, comprises strategic nuclear bombers, submarine-based ballistic missiles and fixed land-based ballistic missiles situated in underground 'hardened' silos. So on top of everything else Britain's four Polaris submarines, which represent the minimum necessary to ensure that at least one vessel is at sea in an operational state at all times, only constitutes one element of the three required to make up a credible deterrent, and with such a small number of vessels it is an extremely vulnerable element at that.

Perhaps most significant of all is the conclusion drawn by American politico-military expert and former US government official Andrew J. Pierre: 'An important lesson of the British experience in the nuclear era is that nations which become dependent on another state's technology do lose some of their perceived political independence.'

In the space of a decade, up to the late nineteen fifties, Britain had taken steps which effectively took her from a position of being on a par with America and Russia as the world's third independent nuclear power to one of nuclear dependence on the United States. At that time nuclear independence was seen to equal the political independence that went with great power status. From the late nineteen fifties onwards Britain's foreign policy has been almost indistinguishable from that of the United States and no major independent politico-military enterprise has been embarked upon which did not have American support.

'The Badge of Our Servitude'

It was widely believed that dependence on America for the continuance of the British deterrent had come about because of economic considerations. The decision to acquire cheaper off-the-shelf delivery systems in place of Blue Streak was interpreted as indicating that Britain could no longer afford to sustain the full costs of keeping her nuclear weapons up to date. The British experience, therefore, seemed to suggest that only Russia and America could afford the luxury of an ongoing independent nuclear deterrent.

This might have remained accepted dogma had it not been for the existence of an alternative model to Britain provided by France. France became the fourth country in the world, after America, Russia and Britain, to possess nuclear weapons, having exploded her first atomic bomb in 1960, although she did not reach the hydrogen bomb stage until 1968. At the same time the French were in the process of developing delivery systems, comprising both manned aircraft and ballistic missiles.

Deemed a 'suitable' ally by the United States, France, too, could have had the American Polaris missile system for her nuclear armoury, an offer which was seen in some quarters as marking the probable end of the 'special relationship' between Britain and America. But the French president, Charles de Gaulle, turned the Americans down. The British experience with the American Skybolt missile, which Britain had relied upon to keep her nuclear deterrent up to date but which the US government arbitrarily cancelled, had signalled the dangers of reliance on a foreign power.

What probably tipped the scales against Polaris for de Gaulle, however, was his suspicion that the American offer was simply a ploy to bring the French deterrent under US control. The acceptance of Polaris by Britain with all its implications, and France's refusal on the grounds that it would jeopardize her nuclear independence, is more than a little ironic because it was Britain's initial nuclear independence which had originally inspired the French to develop a deterrent of their own.

All the main arguments used to advance the cause of the British independent deterrent – the ultimate defence of the nation, the frustration of American/Soviet world hegemony and freedom of action in international politics – were deemed applicable in the case of France, but with the additional suggestion that the French nuclear force might serve as the kernel of a future European defence system.

Like its British counterpart, the French deterrent also fitted the 1962 American definition of 'relatively weak national nuclear forces . . . operating independently' which it was United States policy to discourage. To this end France was subjected to considerable pressure by the Americans to abandon her nuclear independence. Such pressures, including President Kennedy describing, in 1963, the establishment of a French independent nuclear deterrent as 'an unfriendly act', merely served to reinforce French resolve.

By 1978 France was announcing the addition of a sixth submarine to her nuclear deterrent force, which also included the two other elements in a modern credible deterrent, strategic bombers and land-based missiles. All owed their existence to the scientific and technical skills, not to mention the political will, of the French and were thus shielded from the obfuscation that afflicted the status of the American-supplied British Polaris fleet as an independent deterrent. At the same time the French president was proudly boasting, without fear of contradiction, that his country was the world's third nuclear power, way ahead of Britain.

But that was not the only outcome of French nuclear independence. The Americans now recognized France's deterrent as an important factor in the defence of Europe because it kept the Russians guessing. 'We are pleased to have such a force in Europe as it adds to the potential uncertainties Moscow must face', said General Alexander Haig, one-time NATO supreme commander in Europe, in

1979. And it is probably because France's nuclear weapons are absolutely her own and she tolerates no foreign military installations on her soil that the country has no significant nuclear weapons protest movement.

Nothing it seems would be allowed to check the progress of France's ongoing independent nuclear deterrent, not even a radical change of government. In March 1981, after twenty-three years of conservative rule inaugurated in 1958 by de Gaulle, under whose aegis the French deterrent came into being, France voted into power a Socialist government, under which the progress in providing France with 'strike power technologically equal to nuclear weapons employed by the United States and Russia' continued unabated.

Like Charles de Gaulle before him the new Socialist president of France, Francois Mitterrand, did not believe that the United States would intervene in a crisis in Europe caused by Soviet aggression. Mitterrand echoed his conservative predecessor in claiming that no American president would put Chicago at risk in order to save Lyon. With this in mind there are those who consider that perhaps Britain might ultimately be forced to look for her defence to the one genuinely independent nuclear power for whom self-interest dictates that the security of Europe should be paramount, and that power is, of course, France.

In spite of what should perhaps have been seen as the humbling example set by France, when the decision was made in 1982 by the Conservatives under Margaret Thatcher on a replacement for Britain's aging strategic nuclear weapons there was no shift in British policy. The American-supplied Polaris missiles in their four American-designed submarines would be superseded by American-supplied Trident missiles again housed in four American-designed submarines.

But even the arch-Conservative, normally unreservedly pro-Thatcher and pro-Anglo-American alliance, *Daily*

Telegraph expressed reservations over the Trident deal. The paper felt that perhaps Britain should develop her own nuclear delivery system or collaborate with France, whose home-grown deterrent was seen as 'the embodiment of the national will and French independence', rather than purchase Trident, which was widely regarded as being, among other objections, 'a disagreeable reminder of our strategic dependence upon America'.

In this respect the objection to Trident was merely a continuation of that same opposition to total and humiliating dependence on the United States first countenanced in the late nineteen fifties. Then, as now, there were those who were unable to suspend disbelief sufficiently to allow them to accept a Conservative government's claim that Britain's American-supplied nuclear deterrent was entirely under the control of the British prime minister, especially as it was now officially referred to as 'an integral part of NATO's strategic nuclear force'.

This time a shot across the government's bows was fired by one of the Tories own ex-ministers, Sir Hugh Fraser, who contended that 'by purchasing Trident we are not primarily adding to our independent status. We are adding four boats to the already colossal striking power of the United States nuclear submarine fleet. We may be boosting our ego, but we are also doing a good service to the American tax payer.'

This view gained in credibility when it was later revealed that Britain would not even be servicing the Trident missiles. Britain's missile maintenance facilities were to be phased out. British Tridents would be returned to the United States for refurbishment and replacements supplied direct from the American stock-pile, just as if the Royal Navy vessels carrying them were indeed part of the US nuclear submarine fleet. But there was one important difference, an American president could, if he so wished, deny Britain Trident missiles at any time in the same way as the wartime Anglo-American nuclear agreement had been broken in 1946. This possibility became more real after the Soviet and American talks at Reykjavik in 1986 when it was felt that the United States might unilaterally sign away Britain's American-supplied strategic nuclear weapons as part of a superpower arms accord.

A broadside against the Trident deal was provided by Shadow Defence Secretary John Silkin:

> We are completely dependent on the United States for missile technology, launch and guidance systems, satellite intelligence and test facilities. We do not have to risk a nuclear Suez to show that independence is an illusion. The Americans would never let us take Trident unless they were completely satisfied that we would never use it in any other way than as they told us to use it. Trident is not Britain's ticket to peace and freedom, it is the badge of our servitude. The sacrifice of our ability to pursue our own foreign policy is but one of the many casualties of Trident.

'Among the Greatest of Our Contributions to Human Welfare'

Although in the first instance the main concentration was on the military application of nuclear power, the harnessing of the atom did not only mean the production of the ultimate means of destruction. There was also the non-military potential of atomic energy which Britain needed to exploit if she was to remain one of the great technical and industrial nations of the world.

The principal development in the use of nuclear power for peaceful purposes was as a replacement for fossil fuels as an energy source. And in this Britain took the lead yet again because it was at Calder Hall on the Windscale nuclear complex (now known as Sellafield) that the world's first large-scale nuclear power station went into operation in 1956.

Calder Hall was capable of producing 75,000 kilowatts an hour, sufficient electricity to meet the then needs of half a million people. It took eleven tons of coal to generate that much electricity. Calder Hall required just over a tenth of an ounce of uranium. Thus, it was believed, would future industrial societies be sustained. Nuclear power would provide a virtually inexhaustible source of energy more cheaply and more cleanly than that produced by the more conventional coal and oil-fired electricity generating stations, although the capital costs would be higher.

Britain had established a two year world lead in the construction of nuclear power plants, with America and Russia following very much in her wake. Not only that, Calder Hall was also the model for the first nuclear power stations to be planned in any country as part of a considered programme of electricity generation from the atom.

The successful commissioning of the world's first large-scale nuclear power station met with the international acclaim it so richly deserved. Britain had, after all, only begun her nuclear programme nine years earlier. And this she had done from modest beginnings on a disused airfield, or as one British official, Sir Oliver Franks, put it, 'with nothing but green fields and grey matter'.

The historical significance of Calder Hall was aptly summarized in the speech delivered by the Queen at the plant's formal opening on 17 October 1956. The sentiments expressed on that day, the day on which Britain opened yet another door on the future, provide a startling prism through which can be assessed the way the country viewed itself in the now almost alien landscape of the mid-nineteen fifties:

For centuries past visionary ideals and practical methods which have gone from our shores have opened up new ways of thought and modes of life for people in all parts of the world. It may well prove to have been among the greatest of our contributions to human welfare that we have led the way in demonstrating the peaceful uses of this new source of power.

But Calder Hall and the other eleven Magnox gas-cooled reactor power stations projected or under construction in the late fifties were only the beginning. Plans were already in hand for the next development; power stations based on the advanced gas-cooled reactor, or AGR. Meanwhile, work was also progressing on a third and even more advanced type of reactor, a fast breeder, which actually breeds more nuclear fuel than it consumes, thereby relieving the pressure on the world's limited supplies of uranium. The fast breeder reactor offered what was seen as possibly the best hope in the long run for the genuinely economic generation of electricity from atomic energy. Britain's prototype fast reactor power station at Dounreay in Scotland went into operation in November 1959. Once again Britain had stolen a march on the other two nuclear powers, America and Russia, because Dounreay was the most advanced fast breeder reactor in the world.

In 1957, the year following the opening of Calder Hall atomic power station, another milestone in the development of applied nuclear energy was passed, or rather was thought to have been passed, when the experimental apparatus ZETA (Zero Energy Thermonuclear Assembly) came into operation at Harwell. Unlike atomic power reactors which operate on fission, the splitting of atoms, ZETA was concerned with fusion, the joining of atoms. What was ultimately hoped for was the harnessing of the power generated by such fusion, from which the thermonuclear or hydrogen bomb had already been produced. Indeed, the process was often referred to as 'harnessing the H-bomb'. It was also referred to as 'power from the ocean' because it utilized the heavy hydrogen (deuterium) from the sea.

Thermonuclear, or fusion, reactions are the source of the heat and light given out by the sun and the stars so their production and control mean, in effect, creating a man-made sun. ZETA, described lyrically as 'a small and potent sun, which glows with promise for the future', was the largest such experimental apparatus in the world in the late fifties and in August 1957 had come closest to achieving the desired results.

However, a controversy, interesting in its implications, surrounded the announcement of this British triumph. ZETA's success was not made public until several months after the event and only then in conjunction with a progress report of the *American* thermonuclear programme, code-named 'Operation Sherwood'. The suspicion that news of a significant British scientific advance, in which better results were achieved at lower costs than in the United States, had been suppressed at the behest of the Americans became widespread throughout British scientific, political and media circles. This was, of course, the time when the Macmillan government was pushing for a renewal of the wartime full nuclear partnership between Britain and the United States. Clearly, and not for the first time, British interests had been sacrificed to political expediency on the altar of the Anglo-American 'special relationship'.

It soon transpired, however, that the results achieved by ZETA were not quite as hopeful as they were first thought to have been. The prospect of the world's energy problems being truly solved for ever by a fuel as plentiful as the heavy hydrogen in the oceans, and which left behind little in the way of radioactive waste products, was still a long way off. Nevertheless, sufficient information had been gained to encourage progress on ZETA's successor, ZETA II, and by 1959 plans were in hand for a third machine, known as ICSE (Intermediate Current Stability Experiment), the like of which existed nowhere else in the world, to be built at a new centre for thermonuclear research at Culham near Oxford.

But the application of nuclear power for peaceful purposes was not confined solely to generating electricity. There were also radioactive isotopes, or more strictly speaking radionuclides, which are normally produced by bombarding certain chemicals with neutrons inside the core of a research nuclear reactor. These radioisotopes, as they are also called, were destined to transform medicine, agriculture, industrial processes and scientific research. As early as 1952 Britain had become the world's chief exporter of radioactive isotopes. At that time most of these 'nuclear tools' emanated from BEPO (British Experimental Pile Operation) which was not only the largest producer of radioisotopes in the world but also the first of a whole ongoing 'family' of such reactors.

Truly, Britain had seized with both hands the opportunities which nuclear power had to offer. By the late nineteen fifties over 1000 British manufacturing companies were directly involved in the nuclear industry. To Britain's export list could now be added a whole range of products from nuclear power plants and research reactors to radioactive isotopes and nuclear expertise generally. And there was a bonus because as with aerospace there was a high degree of interdependence between the progress of nuclear power and the development of new materials, manufacturing techniques, instrumentation and electronics, such as computers. For instance, Atlas, the world's largest and fastest computer was installed at Harwell in 1961 to aid atomic research.

As Sir Solly Zuckerman observed at the time in relation to nuclear energy: 'The kind of technological world which is unfolding has come at a time when Britain is trying to prevent herself from slipping too far from her position as the oldest, and recently the leading, world power.' While Sir Edwin Plowden, the then chairman of the United Kingdom Atomic Energy Authority, in advocating that Britain must continue to develop nuclear power 'with energy and faith', prophesied that 'the alternative is not to go on as we are. For a nation that has to live by industry in a competitive world the alternative is to become progressively poorer and less secure.'

More Blunder and Confusion

Ostensibly the sun seemed still to shine on Britain's nuclear endeavours in the late nineteen sixties, as it had done in the fifties. Britain was generating more nuclear power than the rest of the world put together and she continued to export nuclear wares and expertise. In short, the atom had become an important element in the economy.

But with what can only be described as grim predictability Britain's civil nuclear programme was already in the process of sharing the same dismal fate as those other areas of advanced technology whose exploitation could, it was believed, check the nation's decline as an economic force and a great power. Once again an enterprise of high promise would founder because of a general lack of direction, commitment and purpose, plus a degree of misfortune.

By the late nineteen seventies Britain's nuclear triumph had turned into nothing short of a fiasco. A mere 14 per cent of the nation's electricity was being derived from atomic energy, only slightly more than in the mid-sixties. According to predictions made in 1956 the figure should have been 50 per cent. The situation had not exactly been improved upon by the constant reappraisals to which Britain's atomic power station programme was subject in the light of ever changing interpretations of the country's projected energy needs. 'We get the demand right – it's just the year we have to change', said one Electricity Council official.

Such was the chaotic condition of the British nuclear power station programme twenty years on from Calder Hall and Britain's undisputed lead in the field that one eminent nuclear engineer, Lord Hinton, was driven to suggest that perhaps Britain ought to abandon her role as a nuclear pioneer and buy reactors from abroad. The future role he envisaged for the country's nuclear industry was that of sub-contractor. This was, of course, the fate that had to a certain extent already befallen the pioneering British aerospace industry.

Again, France provides the contrasting success to Britain's failure. One of the first visits to a foreign country paid by Margaret Thatcher following her election victory in May 1979 was to France where she gazed in utter astonishment at that country's nuclear technology. And well she might. The French nuclear power programme, which began as recently as 1970, is the most ambitious in the western world and will ultimately represent the highest concentration of nuclear reactors (home-developed, albeit based on original American designs) on Earth. To the French government France had 'no serious alternative to nuclear energy except economic recession and dependence on the outside world'.

So impressed was Prime Minister Thatcher by what she saw in France that on her return she declared, almost as if it had never been thought of before, that Britain's real future for the provision of energy lay in building more nuclear power stations. Plans were made to emulate France and other Continental countries that were aiming at an almost total reliance on nuclear power for generating electricity by the end of the century. Subsequently, in December 1979, a new nuclear programme for Britain, the fifth since 1955, was announced. 'I would say that the risks of not going ahead with expanded nuclear power were as great as the risks of cutting off oxygen to the body', the then energy minister said of Britain's latest nuclear programme. The consequence of default would be in his view 'lower living standards for us all and a very severe constraint on our society'. These were, of course, precisely the same sentiments as those expressed a quarter of a century earlier in the mid-nineteen fifties at the launching of Britain's first nuclear programme.

This time though the mainstay would not be British gas-cooled reactors, as had been the case in the previous four programmes, but American reactors of the pressurized water variety. This was notwithstanding the fact that in 1977 a Commons Select Committee on Science and Technology had urged that Britain should stick to her own nuclear technology and avoid switching in midstream.

But ever since the nineteen fifties there had been advocates for the adoption of the American pressurized water, instead of the British gas-cooled, reactor and their lobbying had further muddied the already murky waters of Britain's nuclear programme by increasing the number of considerations that the government had to face. Their cause was strengthened by the fact that the British gas-cooled reactors had displayed little export potential, partly because they had to be built on site. The American pressurized water reactors, or PWRs, on the other hand, were prefabricated and thus completion dates were very reliable and costs could be kept down. Also, unforeseen engineering problems had arisen when the highly successful prototype second generation advanced gas-cooled reactor was scaled up to much larger commercial proportions. This, coupled with catastrophic industrial disputes, had resulted in one particularly notorious AGR power station, Dungeness 'B', taking eighteen years to build instead of six.

So within a generation of establishing a clear world lead in the use of the atom to generate electricity Britain was to be dependent on American hand-me-down nuclear technology. And for the first British PWR at Sizewell the pressure vessel was to be French and other key components Japanese.

Meanwhile the French nuclear programme continued to forge ahead. By 1984 they had no fewer than thirty-two nuclear power plants in operation (twice as many as in Britain) with a further twenty-eight under way. In the process France, the world's leading nuclear power economy, had become not only a primary source of cheap electricity for other European countries, including Britain, but also a major exporter of nuclear technology.

Nineteen eighty-four, incidentally, also saw the launching of an ambitious programme in India to build twenty-two new nuclear power stations by the year 2000, with more than 90 per cent of the equipment for the plant being made in India. And an agreement was signed which opened the door for the export of nuclear technology to China from Japan. (Japan, like France, sees nuclear power as essential to maintaining living standards and as a means of freeing the nation from reliance on the volatile Middle East for its energy needs.) Although initially relying on imported technology, not just Japanese but also French, West German and American, China (nuclear motto: 'To build a strong country, build nuclear power plants') intends eventually to become self-reliant and even an exporter of nuclear wares and know-how.

In France, on top of everything else, rapid progress was being made towards the construction of a commercially viable fast breeder reactor. The same was happening in America, Japan and West Germany. By contrast Britain's own fast breeder programme, which had been responsible for establishing a world lead in this potentially profitable field with the Dounreay prototype reactor in the late fifties, was more or less moribund. In 1983 the decision had been taken to abandon Britain's independent effort in favour of joining an international project led by the French. But within a very short time there were reports of government disenchantment with the scheme, which became prone to technical problems, prolonged delays and the sort of disagreements which almost inevitably afflict international projects.

As to thermonuclear power, offering safe and relatively clean energy for which the oceans of the world would provide a virtually inexhaustible source of fuel, fulfilment failed to match the more optimistic forecasts of the late fifties. At that time, when Britain's ZETA was the world's largest and most advanced thermonuclear experimental apparatus, the conclusion was that the commercial application stage of thermonuclear power could be reached within ten years if everything went perfectly but fifty years if it did not. Thirty-odd years later fifty years seems to have been the most realistic estimate. The 'break-even' point, when a thermonuclear reactor starts to create more energy than has to be put in and thermonuclear 'ignition' takes place, has not yet been reached, not in Britain, America, Russia, nor France, where research began much later than in the first three countries.

But the race for economical thermonuclear power is still on. To this end Culham has become the centre for western Europe's first, and the world's largest, thermonuclear device, JET (Joint European Torus), and it is into this international project that the British effort has now largely been absorbed. Thermonuclear projects in America and Russia have, as one might expect, remained purely national projects. The same is true of Japan, very late in the field and hoping to learn from the mistakes of others. However, such is going to be the cost of developing a successful commercial thermonuclear reactor that only an unprecedented programme of co-operation between western Europe, Japan, America and Russia is now expected to achieve results.

Despite the demise or absorption into multi-national ventures of much of Britain's outstanding nuclear endeavours all is not completely lost because of certain important outcrops of the nuclear industry. British Nuclear Fuels Limited (BNFL) has managed to establish a world lead in the sale of nuclear fuel and in the reprocessing of this same material for other countries' reactors. It has been calculated that by the end of the eighties decade Britain's nuclear fuel business will be a £1000m-plus a year industry and might well have cornered half of the world reprocessing market.

Britain's continuing success in the production of radioactive isotopes can be gauged from the response to the government's sale in 1982 of shares in the hitherto wholly state-owned company, Amersham International, which markets radioisotopes. The offer, nearly twenty-five times over-subscribed, caused a stampede on the stock exchange and the flood of money into the coffers of the Exchequer threatened London money markets with sizeable shortages. But then the projected potential for growth of Amersham International was, after all, 10 per cent faster than that of the British economy as a whole.

The atom, or rather what is left to Britain of the fruits of that dazzling display of nuclear ingenuity in the fifties, remains an important element in the economy. All of which gives legitimacy to the speculation that had Britain's nuclear progress, 'the key to the future' as it was called in 1956, been universally pursued with the 'energy and faith' then advocated it could well have made a major contribution to checking the country's industrial decline, as it was predicted it might.

As it is, disenchantment in Britain with things nuclear has become widespread. More than thirty years on from Calder Hall it has been officially admitted for the very first time that Britain has reaped no economic benefits from her generation of electricity by nuclear power, which *still* represents only a fraction of the country's energy needs. And all this against a backdrop of the Harrisburg and Chernobyl disasters and Britain's own unenviable nuclear pollution record, the full extent of which is only now being revealed after three decades of damaging concealment.

5

CONCLUSION

'Nearly all the great developments of this age of ours have come from this small island, and with a magnanimous hand we have given them to others to help develop for the benefit of mankind at large.' These were the uncompromising terms in which the Engineers' Association president expressed the prevailing sense of pride in Britain's achievements in 1952.

But this very same decade would witness the last great flowering of that genius in the fields of science and technology (as often as not accomplished on the slimmest of budgets) for which Britain had been renowned. The subsequent virtual abandonment of an independent aircraft industry, the total abandonment of a space effort worthy of the term, the relinquishment of a genuinely independent nuclear deterrent and the chaotic condition of the country's atomic energy programme naturally played a major role in the process. Such a drastic curtailment of involvement in the highest forms of technology, the 'big sciences', was bound to affect the general level of Britain's scientific and technological endeavours on the premise that when the tide ebbs all the boats in the harbour drop. The nineteen fifties also witnessed Britain's last hour in the first rank of the world's military and industrial powers; the very state of affairs that a proper exploitation of her science and technology was supposed to prevent.

World War II, the subsequent Cold War and the threat of another world conflict provided the impetus for the development of Britain's superpower technology. The impression gained is that in the process this technology was pushed beyond the competence and even the understanding of the country's decision makers, both elected and unelected, many of whom were the products of what was becoming increasingly regarded as an antiquated social structure with outmoded cultural values. Certainly, many of those who looked for a reason for Britain's failure to compete in areas of traditional industrial activity were drawn more and more to the conclusion that British society and its institutions were set in a mould that was incompatible with what was required of a successful industrial state in the late twentieth century. And the foregoing chapters would seem to suggest that the same conclusion can be drawn with regard to the failure to exploit with assurance and determination Britain's post-war aerospace and nuclear technology. In short, the country's decision makers did not know where to go with it; a condition which seems to have had its origins after the immediate danger of another war receded following the Korean armistice of July 1953.

This would appear to be one of the most compelling reasons, if not *the* most compelling reason, for those catastrophic decisions taken in the latter half of the fifties decade which effectively curbed Britain's technological advance. Perhaps the technology was too much a product of the 'secret vigour and pulse like a cannon', which one nineteenth century American, Ralph Waldo Emerson, reckoned Britain possessed 'in a storm of battle and calamity', to survive in the relatively tranquil (albeit still dangerous and uncertain) world of the later nineteen fifties.

As it was Britain had sown the seeds of the postwar new scientific age but much of the fruits of her labours went to others. Ironically it is what little there is left to the country of its advanced technology pursuits from this period which represent the few bright stars in Britain's decaying industrial firmament of the last quarter of the twentieth century.

Irony is compounded with poignancy by the fact that advanced industrial nations like West Germany and Japan, whose economies had hitherto relied on the application of technology as a means of improving traditional industrial processes, as well as Third World countries, which had missed out on that particular phase of industrialization altogether, now look for their future survival to that same aerospace and nuclear technology which Britain once possessed in plenty but frittered away.

Even so there are those who might still argue that a full, independent exploitation of this sort of advanced technology could never have proved the salvation of a country already in decline. But any such notion can be instantly discounted by the existence of that alternative model to Britain, France, whose rise as a force in the world has been as meteoric as Britain's concomitant decline has been cataclysmic. Yet in certain respects the postwar experience of Britain and France was not dissimilar. The influence and power of both nations had rested on an empire which was lost to them in the decade-and-a-half following the end of World War II. Unlike Britain though France was only a power of secondary rank with no claim to being one of the 'big three' and she was not in the vanguard of the new advanced technology which burgeoned in the postwar world. Neither had France been the world's first industrial state and she had never been the world's premier trading nation. In fact, right up to World War II France was primarily an agrarian society and not really a fully-fledged modern 'developed' nation at all.

As for the nineteen fifties, this decade saw France traumatized and totally demoralized by the bloodiest of retreats from empire and politically very much the 'sick man of Europe'. Yet the French nation was about to begin a recovery from national decline that would ultimately result in France becoming the world's fourth largest industrial democracy, ahead of Britain. And this metamorphosis would be accomplished with the aid of that very technology on which Britain, whose concurrent experience provided the world with the most compelling example of rapid peacetime political, military and industrial decline of modern times, turned her back and thereby distanced herself from the forces shaping the times in which we live.

But then France adapted to the realities of the late twentieth century whereas Britain did not. During the nineteen fifties and sixties the French underwent a profound social and economic transformation designed specifically to fit the nation for the modern world. In the process, British historian Paul Johnson tells us, 'President Charles de Gaulle and his successors, during their rule of nearly a quarter of a century, took France through a second industrial revolution and endowed her with a high-technology base the British have good reason to envy'. And it was a technology nurtured by a competent, technically-minded civil service. This is in sharp contrast to the British civil service which seems almost to pride itself on its ignorance of matters technical.

The motivation behind France's national regeneration was the desire to regain world status. Linked to this was a perception of the need to be independent. It paid handsome dividends. Certainly in her determination to pursue her own interests without constraint France has been free of that enfeebling dependence on, and subordination to, the United States which has so manifestly affected Britain. The French too, unlike the British, have been ever mindful of the threat to national sovereignty posed by a heavy reliance on technology which is in the gift of a foreign power, no matter how friendly, and the similar inherent danger in becoming its technological appendage.

Truly there is a lesson to be learned from the dramatic reversal in France's seemingly insoluble decline and the way in which this was accomplished. Britain certainly possessed the means far in excess of France to accomplish the same change in her fortune but as has been made all too painfully obvious the country's decision makers failed to meet the technological challenges of the postwar world. The result was indeed a crime against the people of Britain.

———————

To say that the task of writing this book was a melancholy experience would be to plumb the depth of understatement. An all-enveloping mood of pessimism, not to mention the inherent dangers in the Arnold Bennett truism that 'pessimism, when you get used to it, is just as agreeable as optimism', could only be kept at bay by constantly keeping in mind what Dickens' Ebenezer Scrooge asked of the Ghost of Christmas Yet to Come:

Men's courses will foreshadow certain ends, to which, if persevered in, they must lead. But if the courses be departed from, the ends will change. Say it is thus with what you show me!

BIBLIOGRAPHY

Unless otherwise stated all works cited are published in London.

AERONAUTICS

Andrews, C. F., *Vickers Aircraft Since 1908* (Putnam, 1969)

Barnes, C. H., *Bristol Aircraft Since 1910* (Putnam, 1964)

Barnes, C. H., *Handley Page Aircraft Since 1907* (Putnam, 1976)

Barnes, C. H., *Shorts Aircraft Since 1900* (Putnam, 1967)

Bowers, Peter M., *Boeing Aircraft Since 1916* (Putnam, 2nd edn, 1968)

Boyne, Walter J. and Lopez, Donald S. (eds), *The Jet Age: Forty Years of Jet Aviation* (Smithsonian Institution, Washington DC, 1979)

Dempster, Derek D., *The Tale of the Comet* (Allan Wingate, 1959)

Encyclopedia of Aviation (Reference International, 1977)

Everett-Heath, John, *British Military Helicopters* (Arms and Armour Press, 1986)

Flight, 13 July 1961

Flight International

Gardner, Charles, *British Aircraft Corporation: A History* (Batsford, 1981)

Gaynor, Frank, *Dictionary of Aerospace* (Peter Owen, 1960)

Gee, Jack, *Mirage: Warplane for the World* (Macdonald, 1971)

Gibbs-Smith, Charles Harvard, *Aviation: An Historical Survey from its Origins to the End of World War II* (HMSO, 1970)

Gill, Ken, 'A Roll as America's Tin-bashers', *Guardian*, 6 April 1981

Green, William, and Fricker, John, *The Air Forces of the World: Their History, Development and Present Strength* (Macdonald, 1958)

Gunston, Bill, *Attack Aircraft of the West* (Ian Allan, Shepperton, 1974)

Gunston, Bill, *Bombers of the West* (Ian Allan, Shepperton, 1973)

Hastings, Stephen, *The Murder of the TSR-2* (Macdonald, 1966)

Jackson, A. J., *Avro Aircraft Since 1908* (Putnam, 1965)

Jackson, A. J., *Blackburn Aircraft Since 1909* (Putnam, 1968)

Jackson, A. J., *British Civil Aircraft Since 1919*, 3 vols (Putnam, 2nd edn, 1973–74)

Jackson, A. J., *De Havilland Aircraft Since 1909* (Putnam, 2nd edn, 1978)

Launay, A. J., *Historic Air Disasters* (Ian Allan, 1967)

Lewis, Peter, *The British Bomber Since 1914* (Putnam, 2nd edn, 1974)

Lewis, Peter, *The British Fighter Since 1912* (Putnam, 2nd edn, 1974)

Lewis, Peter, *British Racing and Record-Breaking Aircraft* (Putnam, 1970)

Mason, David (ed.), *Flight International Directory of Aviation* (1983)

Mason, Francis K., *Hawker Aircraft Since 1920* (Putnam, new edn, 1971)

The Military Balance 1986–1987 (International Institute for Strategic Studies, 1986)

Monday, David (ed.), *The International Encyclopedia of Aviation* (Octopus, 1977)

Morpurgo, J. E., *Barnes Wallis: A Biography* (Longman, 1972)

Myles, Bruce, *Jump Jet: The Revolutionary V/STOL Fighter* (Brassey's, 1978)

Paton, J. O. G., *The British Defence Industry* (Jordan, 1981)

Payne, L. G. S., *Air Dates* (Heinemann, 1957)

Plowden Committee on Aviation, Report of

Reed, Arthur, *Britain's Aircraft Industry: What Went Right? What Went Wrong?* (Dent, 1973)

Spectator, 23 August 1975

Swanborough, F. G., *Combat Aircraft of the World* (Temple Press, 1962)

Swanborough, Gordon, *Military Aircraft of the World* (Ian Allan, Shepperton, 1981)

Swanborough, Gordon, and Bowers, Peter M., *United States Aircraft Since 1908* (Putnam, new edn, 1971)

Sweetman, Bill, *Observer*, 22 February 1981

Taylor, H. A., *Fairey Aircraft Since 1915* (Putnam, 1974)

Taylor, J. W. R. and Moyes, Philip J. R., *Pictorial History of the RAF: Volume Three, 1945–1969* (Ian Allan, 1970)

Taylor, J. W. R. and Swanborough, Gordon, *Military Aircraft of the World* (Ian Allan, 2nd edn, 1973)

Taylor, J. W. R. and Munson, Kenneth (eds), *Aircraft Identification Guide* (New English Library, 1974)

Taylor, J. W. R., Taylor, M. J. H. and Monday, D. (eds), *The Guinness Book of Air Facts and Feats* (Guinness Superlatives, Enfield, 3rd edn, 1977)

Thetford, Owen, *Aircraft of the Royal Air Force Since 1918* (Putnam, 6th edn, 1976)

Thetford, Owen, *British Naval Aircraft Since 1912* (Putnam, 3rd rev. edn, 1971)

Times Survey of British Aviation Supplements

Wallis, B. N., 'The Strength of England', *The Advancement of Science*, vol. 22, no. 101, November 1965

Watt, D. Cameron, 'Demythologizing the Eisenhower Era' in Wm. Roger Louis and Hedley Bull (eds), *The 'Special Relationship': Anglo-American Relations Since 1945* (Oxford University Press, 1986)

Wood, Derek, *Project Cancelled: A Searching Criticism of the Abandonment of Britain's Advanced Aircraft Projects* (Macdonald and Jane's, 1975)

Wragg, David W., *Helicopters at War: A Pictorial History* (Robert Hale, 1983)

Wragg, David W. (comp.), *A Dictionary of Aviation* (Osprey, Reading, 1973)

MISSILES AND SPACE

Aeroplane, vol. 92, no. 2378, 29 March 1957

Allward, Maurice (advisory ed.), *The Encyclopedia of Space* (Paul Hamlyn, 1968)

Allward, Maurice, 'Britain's Guided Missiles and Rockets', *Spaceflight*, vol. 1, no. 4, July 1957

Allward, Maurice, 'The Space Age is Here', *Spaceflight*, vol. 1, no. 6, January 1958

Annual Report of the Advisory Council on Scientific Policy, 1958–1959 (HMSO, 1959)

Baker, David, *The Rocket: The History and Development of Rocket and Missile Technology* (New Cavendish Books, 1978)

Bartlett, C. J., *The Long Retreat: A Short History of British Defence Policy, 1945–1970* (Macmillan, 1972)

Besserer, C. W. and Besserer, Haze C. (eds), *Guide to the Space Age* (Pitman, 1960)

'Britain's Aerospace Industry', *Flight International*, 21 July 1979

Brundrett, Sir Frederick, 'Rockets, Satellites and Military Thinking', *Journal of the United Service Institution,* vol. CV, no. 619, August 1960

Canby, Courtlandt, *A History of Rockets and Space* (Leisure Arts, 1964)

Eberle, James, and Wallace, Helen, *British Space Policy and International Collaboration* (Chatham House Papers, no. 42, Royal Institute of International Affairs/Routledge and Kegan Paul, 1987)

Fairley, Peter, *British Inventions of the 20th Century* (Hart-Davis, 1972)

Gatland, Kenneth W., *Astronautics in the Sixties: A Survey of Current Technology and Future Development* (Iliffe Books, 1962)

Gatland, Kenneth W. (ed.), *Spaceflight Technology: Proceedings of the First Commonwealth Spaceflight Symposium Organised by the British Interplanetary Society 1959* (Academic Press, 1960)

Gilpin, Robert, *France in the Age of the Scientific State* (Princeton University Press, New Jersey, 1968)

Harris, Kenneth, *Observer*, 8 May 1983

Massey, Harrie, and Robins, M. O., *History of British Space Science* (Cambridge University Press, 1986)

Pretty, Ronald (ed.), *Jane's Pocket Book of Missiles* (Macdonald and Jane's, 1975)

Ridpath, Ian (ed.), *The Illustrated Encyclopedia of Astronomy and Space* (Macmillan, 1976)

Scambary, Rex, 'Platform into Space', *Spaceflight*, vol. II, no. 6, April 1960

Shepherd, L. R., 'Britain's Part in Exploring Space', *The Aeroplane*, vol. 96, no. 2471, January 1959

Southall, Ivan, *Woomera* (Angus and Robertson, Sydney, 1962)

Wilding-White, T. M. (ed.), *Jane's Pocket Book of Space Exploration* (Macdonald and Jane's, 1976)

Williams, Beryl, and Epstein, Samuel, *The Rocket Pioneers* (Lutterworth, 1957)

NUCLEAR POWER

Barnaby, Frank, *Man and the Atom: The Uses of Nuclear Energy* (Thames and Hudson, 1971)

Barnaby, Frank, *The Nuclear Age* (Stockholm International Peace Research Institute, 1974)

Bertram, Christoph, *The Future of Strategic Deterrence* (Macmillan, 1981)

Burn, Duncan, *The Political Economy of Nuclear Energy* (Institute of Economic Affairs, 1967)

Epstein, Leon D., 'Britain and the H-bomb, 1955–1958', *Review of Politics*, vol. 21, no. 3, July 1959

Friedman, Norman, 'Is the Nuclear Submarine Really Invulnerable?' *Defence*, vol. XIII, nos. 1/2, January/February 1982

Goldberg, Alfred, 'The Atomic Origins of the British Nuclear Deterrent', *International Affairs*, vol. 40, no. 3, July 1964

Goldschmidt, Bertrand, *The Atomic Adventure*, transl. Peter Beer (Pergamon Press, Oxford, 1964)

Gowing, Margaret, *Britain and Atomic Energy, 1939–1945* (Macmillan, 1964)

Gowing, Margaret (assisted by Lorna Arnold), *Independence and Deterrence: Britain and Atomic Energy, 1945–1952*, 2 vols (Macmillan, 1974)

Groves, Leslie R., *Now It Can Be Told: The Story of the Manhattan Project* (Andre Deutsch, 1963)

Hinton, Lord, 'Two Decades of Nuclear Confusion', *New Scientist*, vol. 72, no. 1024, 28 October 1976

Hogerton, John F., *The Atomic Energy Deskbook* (Chapman and Hall, 1963)

Huntington, Samuel P., *The Common Defense: Strategic Programs in National Politics* (Columbia University Press, New York, 1961)

Jay, Kenneth, *Calder Hall: The Story of Britain's First Atomic Power Station* (Methuen, 1956)

Jay, Kenneth, *Nuclear Power: Today and Tomorrow* (Methuen, 1956)

Kohl, Wilfrid L., *French Nuclear Diplomacy* (Princeton University Press, New Jersey, 1971)

Labour Party Conference 1957, Report of

Long, G., Price, D. and Sowden, R. G., *The New Power* (George Newnes, 1962)

Longstaff, R. M., 'Science and the Development of Nuclear Energy', *Highlights of British Science* (Royal Society, 1978)

Menaul, Stewart, *Countdown: Britain's Strategic Nuclear Forces* (Robert Hale, 1980)

Mendl, Wolf, *Deterrence and Persuasion: French Nuclear Armament in the Context of National Policy, 1945–1969* (Faber and Faber, 1970)

Mendl, Wolf, 'The Background of French Nuclear Policy', *International Affairs*, vol. 41, no. 1, January 1965

Moore, R. V. (ed.), *Nuclear Power* (Institution of Electrical Engineers Monograph Series 6, Cambridge University Press, 1971)

Owen, Sir Leonard, 'Nuclear Engineering in the United Kingdom – The First Ten Years', *Journal of the British Nuclear Energy Society*, vol. II, no. 1, January 1963

Patterson, Walter C., *Nuclear Power* (Penguin, Harmondsworth, 1976)

Payne, George Louis, *Britain's Scientific and Technological Manpower* (Oxford University Press, 1960)

Pierre, Andrew J., *Nuclear Politics: The British Experience with an Independent Strategic Force, 1939–1970* (Oxford University Press, 1972)

Riedman, Sarah R., *Men and Women Behind the Atom* (Scientific Book Club, 1957)

Rosecrance, R. N., *Defense of the Realm: British Strategy in the Nuclear Epoch* (Columbia University Press, New York, 1968)

Thonemann, P. C., *et al*, 'Controlled Release of Thermonuclear Energy', *Nature,* vol. 181, no. 4604, 25 January 1958

Times Calder Hall Supplement, 17 October 1956

Wallace, William, 'World Status Without Tears' *in* Vernon Bogdanor and Robert Skidelsky (eds), *The Age of Affluence, 1951–1964* (Macmillan, 1970)

Williams, Francis, *A Prime Minister Remembers* (Heinemann, 1961)

Zuckerman, Sir Solly, 'Postscript' *in* Harrison Brown, James Bonner and John Weir, *The Next Hundred Years* (Weidenfeld and Nicolson, 1957)

GENERAL

Bayliss, John (ed.), *British Defence Policy in a Changing World* (Croom Helm, 1977)

Blondel, J., 'Contemporary France: Politics, Society and Institutions' *in* D. G. Charlton (ed.), *France: A Companion to French Studies* (Methuen, 1972)

Defence White Papers, 1955, 1957, 1958, 1959

Grosvenor, Peter, and McMillan, James, *The British Genius* (Dent, 1973)

Labour Party Conference 1963, Report of

Parliamentary Debates (Hansard)

Sampson, Anthony, *Anatomy of Britain* (Hodder and Stoughton, 1962)

Villa, Leo, and Gray, Tony, *The Record Breakers: Sir Malcolm and Donald Campbell, Land and Water Speed Kings of the 20th Century* (Hamlyn, 1969)

INDEX